Circuit Overload

*The bumper book of circuits
for the radio amateur*

John Fielding, ZS5JF

Radio Society of Great Britain

Published by the Radio Society of Great Britain, Cranborne Road, Potters Bar, Herts EN6 3JE.

First published 2006

ISBN: 1-905086-20-2
EAN: 9781905086207

Publisher's note

The opinions expressed in this book are those of the author and not necessarily those of the RSGB. While the information presented is believed to be correct, the author, the publisher and their agents cannot accept responsibility for consequences arising from any inaccuracies or omissions.

Cover design: Dorotea Vizer
Editing, typography and design: Steve Telenius-Lowe, 9M6DXX
Production: Mark Allgar, M1MPA

Printed in Great Britain by Page Brothers of Norwich

Contents

Introduction

- The cost of construction
- Component values & ratings
- Printed circuit boards
- The 'breadboard'
- Buy in bulk!
- Surface mount devices
- Lead-free solder

MANY radio amateurs have never built anything during their time in the hobby. This rather startling and damning admission is largely because they have never bothered to show the interest in what is after all a hobby in the self-training in electronics and radio telecommunications. It could also be because the items they have in their shack have been purchased and so there was no need to learn how to build them. Sadly, in my opinion, the amateur radio hobby has become more and more a 'cheque-book hobby' or as more than one writer calls it, the domain of the 'black-box operator'.

It is hoped that this book will encourage the average radio amateur to attempt the construction of some item that will be useful around the shack and add to the gathering of knowledge in this fascinating hobby.

Because this book is aimed at what we might call 'the beginner' (although the amateur may have been licensed for some time), the circuits to be presented will be of a basic type. So do not expect to find complex multi-mode transceivers within these pages. However, many smaller portions of circuitry can be inter-connected to make a more complex item; it rests with the ability and ingenuity of the reader to pursue this aspect. When some experience and confidence have been gained in building simple circuits, the reader will find that more complex circuits will not have the same daunting look. As skill develops further the reader will find that more complex circuits will appear to be simpler and they will then wonder what all the fuss was about earlier.

I have broken down the many circuits into logical types covering many of the items that the average radio amateur may find useful.

The cost of construction

The intention from the outset was to limit the cost of the components used to that which the average amateur is likely to be able to afford. Hence, where it is possible to do so, I have chosen commonly available integrated circuits and other semiconductors that can be purchased from suppliers or may be found for sale at amateur mobile rallies or flea markets.

Originally when the idea for this book first germinated in my mind I had the intention of setting a cost limit on the components of, say, £5 or $10, but I soon realised that this was not going to work if the components are purchased in one-off quantities. It also somewhat limits the types of circuit that could be offered. I haven't given any form of pricing for the various circuits, as this will greatly depend on where you purchase the components and whether they are new stock or 'recycled' via a mobile rally or flea market vendor.

Often it is possible to pick up good components for next to nothing if you have your wits about you and know what you are looking for. A good source is second-hand printed circuit boards from common items like photocopiers, video cassette recorders and other domestic items. Often these turn up at mobile rallies or flea markets crammed with exotic components that we would never be able to afford if bought new. By carefully 'harvesting' the devices from the boards we can build up a stock of really nice components for next to nothing. Of course there is no guarantee that all the components will still *work*, but it is worth the effort considering how little you are paying for the scrap board.

Component values & ratings

I have taken the time and trouble to choose the circuits so that they are fairly tolerant to component value variations. In many circuits the use of 5% or 10% tolerance capacitors and resistors will be adequate and several different semiconductors should work without any difficulty. For example I often use the BC337 NPN transistor in my day-to-day designs because it is readily available and a low cost item that I carry as a stock item for my other products. Several other devices will also work, for example BC107, BC108, BC109, 2N2222 etc. I have also stuck to E12 values for resistors and capacitors in the interest of greater availability and lower cost. When designing I normally try to limit my stock inventory to a few common devices because I use such a large volume I can often use a common device in many different products. This means that when I have to restock I am buying larger quantities of just a few devices, which all helps to keep the cost down because I get better discounts for large quantities.

Throughout this book the ratings of components will only be

mentioned where they differ from normal types. For example, all the resistors may be 1/4W or 1/2W types with a tolerance of 5% or better, except where mentioned. The same goes for capacitors; where a capacitor has a particular feature it will be detailed. For other capacitors if they are electrolytics the working voltage is normally selected to be above the supply voltage, so for most circuits 25V or less will be suitable. For small capacitor values, for example 10nF or 100nF, the normal working voltage is usually 50V. Where high voltages are used the capacitor working voltage should be chosen to be above the maximum working voltage.

Printed circuit boards

The other major cost item in most circuits is the printed circuit board. When a one-off item is required it is not generally economic to resort to a printed circuit board. Although with etch resist pens and other methods a one off board could be made at home, these days I don't bother to try to make one.

The tooling costs for a printed circuit board are often more than the cost of the finished board, hence we end up paying several times more than the board warrants. Tooling costs are a one-off charge made by the printed circuit manufacturer and cover items such as the setting-up, photographing of the artwork and reducing it to the final size, the generation of drilling tapes or other data and the silk screening and solder mask, if required. Once you have paid this initial tooling cost, in any subsequent orders you are only charged for the cost of the board and labour, provided the board artwork does not change. If you need to change anything you pay another set of tooling charges, so if going down this route be extra careful your artwork is correct before sending it off for processing - or it can be an expensive exercise.

Try to limit the number of different hole sizes needed, as every time a different drill size is needed the cost goes up because the drills need to be changed, which for some manufacturers is a manual task. Also, glass fibre printed circuit board is quite abrasive and so the drills used are made of expensive tungsten carbide which have a limited life. It is therefore normal to factor into every job a wastage cost for drills.

If you intend to make a small production run, the outlook changes and the tooling cost can be amortised over the quantity, making the unit cost somewhat lower. Several members of your local radio club could get together and jointly purchase a quantity of printed circuit boards and components in bulk to reduce the cost.

To give some indication of the costs involved I will use as an example a small printed circuit board that I have manufactured for an automotive product I sell. This board measures 100 x 50mm and is a double sided through hole plated board with solder mask and silk screen identification. The unit cost of the board in quantities of 25 off is about R16.00 (about £1.18) each, but the tooling costs are R300.00 each time I make a change, so I try to avoid this as much as possible. So for the first off run of 25 boards I pay R700.00 which works out to R12.00 tooling amortised on each board, or a unit cost of R28.00 per board. If I only require 10 boards the tooling cost per board goes up to R30.00, making the total cost of the board R46.00. If you intend making small production runs it is beneficial to talk to the board manufacturer first to get a scale of their charges, you might be unpleasantly surprised otherwise.

The 'breadboard'

I will show the reader several different ways of how to make what design engineers call a 'breadboard' for a one-off item. In 99% of cases a breadboard will do all that we require and if the reader thinks it doesn't look too pretty then it is simple to fit the breadboard into a commercial box to hide it from view. Some of my past colleagues were expert in making complex breadboards that not only worked well but looked like works of art and it was a shame to hide them away in a box.

Buy in bulk!

Buying in one-off quantities is often not the best way to buy components. Buying in bulk is a much better way if the funds run to it. Often a supplier will have MOQ (*minimum order quantity*) restrictions and we may find that if we buy 10 or more components it is much cheaper, provided you think you will be needing the item again in the future.

Typically, price breaks run might something like this: 1 to 9 pcs, 10 to 19 pcs, 20 to 49 pcs, 50 and up. So if you ask the supplier in the correct way you may find it cheaper to buy 10 pieces and they will cost less than buying just the five you need immediately.

It is always a good idea to have a few spare components on hand in case you encounter a problem and need to change one. There is nothing more frustrating than finding on the weekend that you need just one transistor to repair something and the supplier only opens again on Monday morning. I would suggest that when buying items like common value resistors and capacitors that you purchase 100 resistors and 25 capacitors. It is surprising how quickly the $10k\Omega$ resistors and 10nF capacitors you bought last month dwindle in number as you build more and more circuits.

Some of the circuits I have adapted from semiconductor manufacturers' application notes or data sheets; in such cases I have endeavoured to acknowledge the original source. In days gone by the possession of data books was something of a closed shop for people who were not involved in electronic design. Today with the Internet available to almost everybody, we have access to this valuable source of information, provided we know where to look.

Surface mount devices

In days gone by, components were predominantly axial or radial leaded devices with long wire leads that needed to be bent to fit into printed circuit boards. In more recent times surface mount devices (SMD) began to appear on the market. This occurred from about the early 1970s. Today the old fashioned leaded component is becoming less popular and the vast majority of today's equipment is manufactured using SMD components. This is driven by the mass market for items such as cellular phones and other high volume items. Although conventional leaded components are unlikely to disappear totally from the market in the foreseeable future, they are gradually becoming harder to find from some suppliers and the cost will inevitably increase as time goes by.

Currently SMD components cost about the same to about 10 to 20% more than conventional components, but the far lower labour cost to assemble the printed circuit board using robot component placers and automated wave soldering gives the high volume manufacturer a distinct edge in this highly competitive market. One of the major costs of a printed circuit board is the drilling of holes; SMD boards need far fewer holes and hence the board unit cost falls accordingly.

SMD components are inherently superior for high frequency operation because of the reduced lead and package parasitics; hence the SMD version of a popular device will often outperform the conventional version in comparable circuits. This is especially the case for frequencies above 1GHz. The cellular telephone industry has moved from the original 450MHz spectrum, through 900MHz, 1.8GHz and now into the 2.4GHz spectrum where many new interesting devices are now available for reasonable costs. The amateur constructor should be enthusiastically investigating this and designing with these better devices. None of these are available in conventional leaded components.

The mainstay for amateur constructors will still be conventional components, because they are easier to handle and solder into a circuit. A factor against a widespread change to SMD by the home constructor in the near future is that the manufacturers of common components such as like capacitors, resistors and semiconductors ship them in reel form and not loose like conventional components. Resistors, diodes and axial leaded capacitors of conventional types are often supplied on a bandoleer tape, often called 'ammo-pack' as they resemble machine gun bullets, with the components connected by the tape strips to hold them in the correct spacing for an automatic insertion machine. SMD components are supplied on 8mm film reels in quantities of 2000, 3000 or as many as 8000 or 10,000 pieces to a reel. Many component wholesalers are reluctant to split reels into smaller quantities because the reel then loses the 'leader-tape' and then they will not work in a robotic placer. Although there are some specialty component suppliers who will split large reels into 100 pieces, the price per component is greater than the normal cost, sometimes by as much as three times. Hence, this somewhat dissuades us from learning about a form of construction that sooner or later we as amateurs will be forced into, as more and more conventional components are discontinued in favour of the SMD version.

Lead-free solder

A very recent development now affecting the electronic manufacturing and component industry is the abolition of lead in solder. From June 2006 it is illegal to manufacture for sale in the European Economic Community (EEC), and many other countries, any item of electronics that contains lead solder.

The directive on RoHS (Restriction of Hazardous Substances) will affect the amateur constructor as the normal tin / lead solder we have been using for the last 90 years will become scarcer and eventually will disappear from the market. Many component manufacturers are now only offering the new solder coating on the components they supply. This requires a change in the manufacturing techniques when components are soldered on a board.

Fortunately, the current RoHS legislation does not affect us as private individuals if we are making an item for our own use. It is only when we manufacture for general sale that the legislation kicks in. The substitute solders now available contain silver or antimony to replace the lead, this of course means that cost increases dramatically, but the usage is much as before. It only requires the soldering iron temperature to be increased a little for the solder to melt and flow correctly. In many cases the joints made with tin / silver solder are as good as or in many cases better than the old 60 / 40 tin / lead solder. Tin / silver solder has been around in the electronics industry for many years for specialised soldering of surface mount devices.

This RoHS directive is a move to reduce the amount of hazardous lead, but the use of solder for electronic and plumbing applications only accounts for about 2% of world use for lead. The vast majority is used in automotive lead-acid batteries and this is unlikely to change in the foreseeable future due to technical difficulties in producing an equivalent battery using another material at an economic price. It seems that well-meaning bureaucrats have saddled us with an unnecessary piece of legislation that will achieve little to reduce lead usage. So if you intend doing any constructing in the future it would be prudent to stock up with the old tin / lead solder while it is still available.

Happy constructing!

John Fielding, ZS5JF

The breadboard

In this chapter:

- The breadboard
- Professional breadboard
- Doughnut board
- Pad strip board
- 'Dead bug' method
- Veroboard
- Home made printed circuit boards

B READBOARDS are an historical throwback to the early days of radio construction. As the name suggests, they were originally a piece of wood used to cut bread on. In the early days of radio home construction the experimenter needed a cheap but sturdy base on which to build the circuit and a breadboard was a cheap and readily available item from most grocery or hardware shops.

The construction began by hammering into the flat wooden breadboard brass panel pins so that they were about 1/4in to 1/2in (6 to 12mm) proud of the surface. With a hot soldering iron the heads of the brass panel pins were tinned and these then served as rigid attachment points for the wires and other components. In later days whole radio receivers were constructed in a similar manner with brass fixtures screwed on to the flat piece of wood to form a rigid and stable base for the item.

However, wood is not the ideal material for this application and today is quite expensive. Although it is nominally a fair insulator if it should get damp the leakage currents, especially when high voltages are used such as in valve equipment, make it less than desirable. It is also difficult to arrange a good low inductance grounding method unless a conducting bus bar is also laid on the wood.

Today we can use different materials, but the principle is still largely the same. A flat sheet of some electrically conducting material is used and the components are attached to the common ground by soldering where needed. A common material is a piece of tin plate salvaged from an old biscuit tin and fixed to a piece of plywood or chip board (MDF) with either panel pins or small wood screws. Another popular choice for the base plate is single-sided printed-circuit board, preferably tin plated. Tin plated steel eventually corrodes and so a better method is to use a non-corrosive material like tin plated copper clad printed circuit board. This with its copper layer forms a good low resistance ground. I favour this method, as off cuts of scrap board are often available free just for the asking from printed circuit board manufacturers. (There is always some waste material involved in printed circuit board manufacture and often the off cuts are too small to be used for other jobs. Hence they are tossed into a scrap bin to be sold at a later date for the small amount of copper they contain). Clean the copper well with some kitchen scouring powder or an abrasive kitchen pad to remove any oxidisation. Often if 1.5mm thick board is used the base plate is stiff enough to not require any further fixing on to wood. If your friendly PCB manufacturer still has one of the older 'roller-tinning' machines it helps to run the cleaned board through this to give a better surface to solder to.

Professional breadboard

There are on the market several professional breadboard materials that can be purchased. The two major types are known in the trade as 'dough-nut board' and 'pad strip board'. In a previous company we used to draw up artworks for both of these and have them made in quantity for the engineers to build prototype circuits on. Examples of the two are shown in **Fig 1.1** and **Fig 1.2** below. The pitch between adjacent holes or pads is 0.1in (2.54mm) because that is the common spacing used for dual inline ICs (DILs).

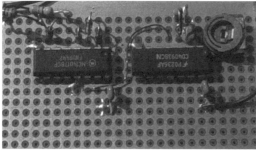

Fig 1.1. Doughnut board – top side

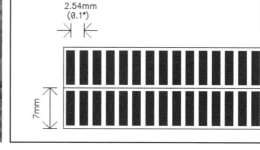

Fig 1.2. Pad strip board

Doughnut board

As the name suggests, the board has a number of holes with corresponding pads on the bottom of the board that look like doughnuts (**Fig 1.3**). The top copper surface of the board has clearance holes for the component leads to pass through. The board is made from 1.5mm thick G-10/FR-4 (glass fibre) material and is double sided tinned copper. The bottom pads are approx 2mm in diameter and the clearance in the top copper is a similar diameter. Hence, the artwork simply consists of the pad layer; producing a negative of the pad layer generates the top copper layer.

The holes drilled in the board are 0.7mm diameter which suits the majority of the normal components. If the component lead is larger, a small drill bit held in a hand pin-chuck is used to open the hole up. Connection between components is either by the component lead itself (e.g. resistor) or self-fluxing enameled copper wire. Where a ground point is needed the IC leg or component lead is bent through 90° and soldered directly to the top copper ground plane.

Doughnut board is a good method to construct RF circuits or complex digital circuits on. With some skill during assembly the layout can be very close to that of the following printed circuit board when finally laid out,

as **Fig 1.5** shows. For digital circuits, where tracks need to sometimes connect over long distances, the use of fine self-fluxing enamel copper wire of about 0.2mm diameter laid on the top surface of the board is the best option.

Fig 1.3. Bottom of doughnut board

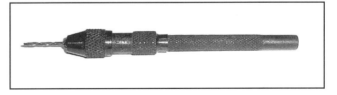

Fig 1.4. Eclipse pin-chuck for small drill bits

Fig 1.5. Typical prototype circuit board made to fit a die cast box

Pad strip board

Originally this was invented by a German company and sold under the name of 'Wainwright Mini-Mount'. Not only were pad strips available but also many other types, such as a small piece of board printed to accept DIL ICs. Today the items are quite expensive, but we can use the idea to make our own strip boards. A picture of a single strip for DIL ICs is shown in **Fig 1.6**.

The board is 7mm wide and approx 125mm long, which allows several ICs to be mounted on each strip. The board material used is single-

Fig 1.6. DIL strip board with 0.1in pitch

sided G-10/FR-4 which is 0.7mm thick and the various strips are printed side by side and the gap between the strips are Vee-scored to allow easy breaking apart. An example of breadboard made using this strip board is shown in **Fig 1.7**.

The pad strips are attached to the printed circuit board with either super-glue or thin double-sided adhesive tape. Another method is to use a small piece of component lead soldered between an IC ground pin across the pad and then continued onto the copper ground plane. The strips of pads can be cut with a pair of old scissors, tin-snips or stout side cutters. To mount DIL ICs the legs of the IC are bent through 90° as shown in **Fig 1.8** opposite. This can be done with a pair of needlenose pliers to grip all the pins on one side of the IC.

Resistors and other components can also be mounted in the same manner with the correct pad strip spacing. Often the best method is first to

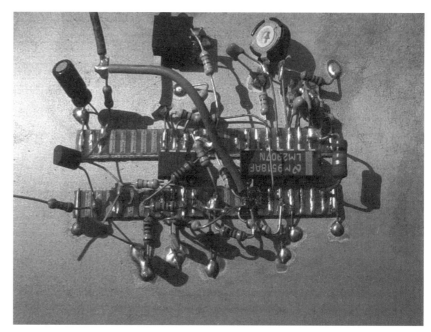

Fig 1.7. Typical breadboard construction

mount the various DIL ICs and leave spaces between adjacent ICs to fit resistors and other axial components, such as diodes. Where a component needs to connect to ground its lead is bent and soldered directly to the ground plane copper.

An alternative method

Some home constructors favour a different approach. This is commonly known as 'dead bug' construction. Here the ICs are fitted upside down so that the pins point upwards and the plastic body is glued to the copper board with a dab of super glue. Where an IC pin needs to connect to ground it is carefully bent so that it can be soldered to the copper. The writer finds this is not a very suitable method because it is difficult to see the pinout of the IC: the pin 1 identifier is normally a notch on the top of the IC package molded in the plastic and with the IC upside down it is difficult to see. I have also become used to working from the top of the board, where the IC pins can be seen clearly. When the printed circuit board layout is made the view is always looking from the top of the board - the component side. With the 'dead bug' method if you need to remove an IC it is a bit tricky, especially if the IC has been super-glued on to the board.

For these reasons I favour the pad strip method over any other; the doughnut board approach means you have to continuously flip the board over to make connections and it is too easy to make a mistake when counting the IC pins from the bottom. By having to work only from one side of the board it makes the job simpler and faster.

Fig 1.8. How IC leads are bent to mount on to pad strip

Veroboard

This was a popular material many years ago and many amateurs built circuits using it. It is a phenolic based material (compressed paper and resin) which has parallel strips of copper running on one side and holes drilled every 0.1in (2.54mm) to connect the component leads. The component side was bare phenolic. In order to separate the strips a special tool somewhat like a drill bit held in a handle was placed on the copper strip so that the point was centered in one of the holes and twisted to remove the copper. Americans know this as 'Perf-board' (perforated board), I haven't seen Veroboard on sale for a while, it may still be available but to be honest I haven't looked that hard for it. The last time I used Veroboard was about 20 years ago.

In use Veroboard is very much like the doughnut board method with the component mounted on the non-coated side of the board. The big limitation was getting a good low inductance ground. I had some special Veroboard some time

Fig 1.9. Veroboard construction

ago that had copper on both sides, the topside was like doughnut board, but I believe this may have been a specially manufactured item for a customer.

Home made printed circuit boards

Sometimes the need exists to make a one-off printed circuit board for a project. Today I don't bother with this because after I have developed the circuit on a breadboard I go straight to a computer generated printed circuit board layout. This then gets e-mailed as a file to my printed circuit board manufacturer. The only time I go to see the company is when I collect the finished boards. The days of plotting on to film and photographically reducing are a thing of the past. Today the board layout is plotted directly on to the photo-master at final size from the computer generated file.

In earlier days we made printed circuit board layouts using pads and tapes on clear Mylar drawing film working on a back lit 'light box'. The light box had a transparent grid sheet attached that was in increments of 0.1in scaled to suit the scale we were working in. Often these were 2:1 or 4:1 of the final size and then they were photographically reduced with a plate camera, such as a Little-John. To assist in placing the pads in the correct places we developed a second transparent film where all the common components in use were drawn with ink on to a Mylar film at 10:1 scale and then reduced photographically to the appropriate scale. This is known as a 'Puppet sheet'. This could be slipped under the other films to

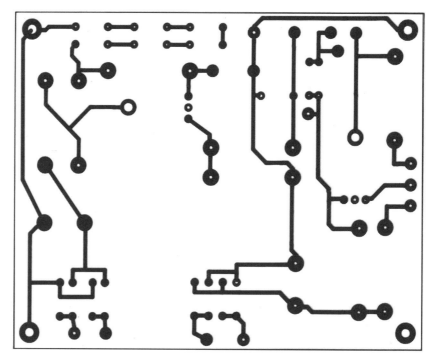

Fig 1.10. Printed Circuit Board artwork on Mylar film

show the exact point where a pad was required. When all the pads were in place we then 'joined up the dots' with tape where the tracks will be.

Before we got to this point, however, we first had to make a rough drawing to scale on several sheets of tracing paper with coloured crayons so we could work out the tracking required. Normally the convention was to use blue for the bottom tracks and red for the top tracks and the components would be drawn in pencil using a stencil. It could take several days (and several abortive permutations) before a workable layout was obtained. After the rough layout was approved the placing of pads and tracks was quite quick. The tracing paper sheets were placed under the Mylar film and lined up with the reference grid from two datum points which were often the corners of the board if it was a rectangular or square shape. Often the board was an odd shape and then two 'tooling holes' were used. Tooling holes are always required in printed circuit board manufacture, especially for stack drilling. Often these tooling holes are placed diagonally opposite and outside the area of the final board. For stack drilling as many as 10 blank boards are placed one on top of the other using dowel pins to line up the boards accurately through the tooling holes. A long series drill is used to drill the entire stack in one plunge of the drill, so ensuring consistent quality. This is one of the reasons so much waste occurs in printed circuit board manufacture, as a wide border of unused material is needed to accommodate the tooling holes.

For a single sided board the artwork consisted of two sheets, one was the pad sheet, which only contained the pads; the second sheet was the tracks. Registration of the two films was by a 'pin bar' which had holes punched to fit on the pin bar. For double-sided boards we used the common pad sheet for top and bottom layers to give the correct registration. If the top copper was mostly solid, as would be the case for an RF layout, then the top copper starts out as a sheet of 'Amberlith' or 'Rubylith' film and the clearance holes need to be cut out with a compass and a special cutting tool. When the circles had been scribed with the correct diameter the unwanted pieces of Amberlith were removed with a sharp scalpel blade to lift the edge and peel them away.

When finally the artwork was complete, the sheets with the pin-bar were transferred to the Little-John plate camera and the various layers photographed and then reduced to 1:1 scale.

The last time I used Amberlith and pads was back in 1988 when we obtained our first computer printed circuit board system.

The drills used for drilling glass fibre printed circuit board are made of solid tungsten carbide and are very fragile. If you drop one on to a concrete floor they can shatter into several pieces. The shanks are normally 1/8in (3.175mm) in diameter, irrespective of the drill size. This is an industry standard for the collet chucks used in high speed drilling machines. The speed the drill is spun at is quite fantastic; a drill 0.5mm in diameter is optimum at about 20,000RPM. The smallest drill commonly available is 0.2mm and this requires a speed of about 40,000RPM. Larger drills require somewhat less but never less than about 8000RPM. The largest commonly available drill is about 1/4in and if larger holes are needed then a small routing cutter is used to cut out the holes.

Using a tungsten carbide drill in a normal drill press that can only spin at 3000RPM maximum is not very productive. Because they are so fragile they cannot tolerate any misalignment and will snap if any side force is used, so drilling with a hobby drill by hand is not advised. To get the very high speeds needed the drilling machine spindle is often supported in 'air-bearings' to reduce the friction. My printed circuit board manufacturer has a fairly new machine that can get up to 80,000RPM if needed. Most high speed drilling machines will drill at the rate of five holes per second when driven by punched tape or a CNC controller.

My friendly printed circuit manufacturer saves the broken drills for me as they make excellent cutters when ground and fastened into a lathe tool holder and will walk through tough materials like chill cast bronze, stainless steel and cast iron when used as a lathe tool. Tungsten carbide is not a recyclable material and so has no intrinsic scrap value. To grind tungsten carbide you need a special 'green-grit' abrasive wheel or a diamond loaded wheel on a tool and cutter grinder; a normal 'grey-grit' grinding wheel or file will not even touch it.

Broken drills inserted in a handle by brazing and suitably ground make excellent cutters and scribing tools for glass and ceramic tiles.

One of the most useful tools I ever bought was about 25 years ago when I was involved in the making of one-off boards for a radio communication system when I worked for one of the Marconi companies. I purchased a set of spot-face cutters to make the top copper clearance. These were used in a small 12V electric hobby drill and used a pilot drill to make the initial hole. The body of the cutter has a small cutter blade that removes the copper in a similar way to the way the Veroboard cutter works. A picture of two cutters is shown in **Fig 1.11**. These were sold by Radio Spares, today called RS Components, and were described as PCB counter-bores.

The pilot drill is 1mm diameter and the cutters make circular clearance holes in the top copper of 2mm or 3mm. The body is split lengthwise to act like a collet so that it grips the pilot drill firmly and they are inserted into the collet chuck of the 12V electric hobby drill.

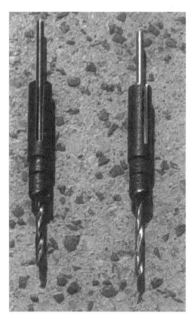

Fig 1.11. Printed circuit board spot-face cutters

CHAPTER 2

Audio circuits

In this chapter:

- A Morse code oscillator
- Audio band pass filter for weak signal reception
- Audio notch filter
- 2W audio amplifier
- 10W audio amplifier
- Audio level monitoring circuit
- Wideband white noise generator
- Simple audio oscillator
- Tuning-up adapter
- Gain controlled audio amplifier
- Audio speech clipper and low pass filter

L ET US start off with a simple Morse code oscillator. I know the gradual phasing out of Morse code as a requirement for a licence is occurring in a lot of countries at present, but lots of amateurs will want to learn Morse code and so will need an oscillator to practice sending.

A Morse code oscillator

There are a great many circuits we could use to make an audio oscillator that can be keyed, some use the NE-555 and others use digital ICs to form the oscillator. Most of the circuits I have tried sound a bit squawky and the note is harsh. This is because the oscillator generates a square wave and loudspeakers react unfavourably to square waves.

So here is my circuit using a dual Operational Amplifier for the oscillator and incorporating a low pass filter to turn the square wave signal into something nearer a sine wave. It also makes a fine oscillator for many other applications where the purity of the sine wave isn't that important. I am sure you can think up lots of applications.

The circuit is built around a National Semiconductors LM358N dual

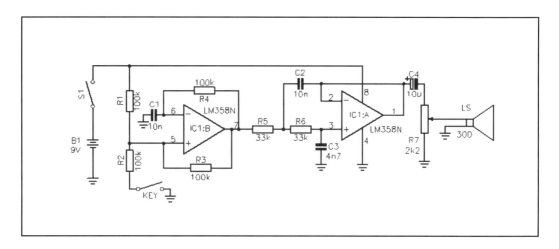

Fig 2.1. A Morse code oscillator

Op-Amp, one of my favorite devices. It is readily available and inexpensive. Almost any of the normal dual op-amps will work here; even a pair of LM741s will do the job. IC1B forms the square wave oscillator with the 100kΩ resistor R4 between the output and the inverting input and C1 determining the frequency. With the values shown the frequency is about 1kHz. If you want to vary the frequency you can either make R4 variable or substitute a different value for C1. Resistors R1 and R2 bias the op-amp to half the supply rail for linear operation. When the key is closed the oscillator runs and drives the second stage audio low pass filter.

IC1A is a unity gain voltage follower with feedback to determine the cut off frequency. R5 and R6 along with C2 and C3 are the components that set the cut off frequency, C3 should be half the value of C2. It is nominally set to about 1.5kHz to reject the 2nd harmonic of the input signal. The signal exiting the second stage is sufficient to drive a high impedance loudspeaker, such as a telephone earpiece. The volume is set by R7, which can be a normal volume control or a preset resistor mounted on the board. The output coupling capacitor C4 can be an aluminium electrolytic, or a tantalum type will also work.

The circuit is powered by a transistor radio battery such as a PP3 or larger. Either fit an on/off switch or simply unplug the battery connector when not in use. If using a small battery like the PP3 an electrolytic capacitor of about 100µF may be needed across the supply rails to prevent 'chirp' when the oscillator is keyed.

Audio band-pass filter for weak signal reception

An audio filter can improve the reception of very weak signals on CW for EME or DX operation. This filter has a very narrow bandwidth and can be fitted between the receiver detector stage and the loudspeaker amplifier in the receiver. Reducing the audio bandwidth from the normal CW filter band-

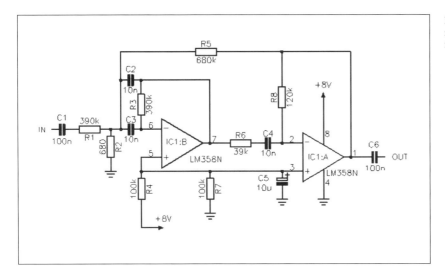

Fig 2.2. A narrow band audio filter

width of 500Hz to 50Hz is a signal to noise improvement of 10dB. If an SSB filter of 2.5kHz is used to receive CW signals, the improvement is even greater with this filter: 50 times as a ratio or 17dB as a log ratio, which is about three 'S' points improvement. This circuit is based on a National Semiconductors application note for the LM158 series of op-amps. It has a centre frequency of about 850Hz, a bandwidth of about 40Hz and a Q of about 25, so it is very sharp.

The op-amps are configured as a multiple feedback network. The main frequency setting components are the 10nF capacitors and the 680Ω resistor (R2) at the input. To change the centre frequency you can make R2 partly variable with a low value 'pot' in series; increasing the value of R2 lowers the centre frequency. The 10nF capacitors C2, C3 and C4 need to be close tolerance types, preferably 5% or better, and the resistors can be 5% or closer tolerance. The best choice for the 10nF capacitors is polycarbonate or polyester such as the types made by Wima. The closer the capacitors and resistors are to the optimum value, the narrower the bandwidth will be. If you have a DVM with a capacitance measuring facility you can select the 10nF capacitors to find three with the same value.

In common with most high Q narrow band filters this one also tends to ring when strong signals are presented to it. The gain from input to output is nominally unity so you may need to attenuate the input signal to reduce the ringing problem.

Audio notch filter

There are many applications where we require a notch filter to eliminate a particular audio frequency. An example might be where you need to strip off the CTCSS sub-audible tone at a repeater receiver before it is retransmitted. This circuit is basically the previous band pass filter inverted to null out an

Fig 2.3. An audio notch filter

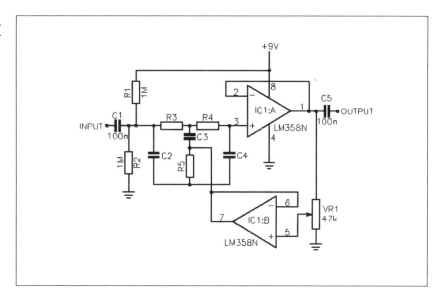

audio tone. Again it is derived from the National Semiconductors application notes on the LM158 series of op-amps. Like the band pass filter it is also extremely sharp, only about 40Hz wide at about 800Hz (5%). Again the tolerance of the capacitors and resistors have a large effect on how deep the null is and how wide the null is. A preset pot is used to set the depth of the null. With careful setting up and selection of components a null of 40dB or more is possible.

The components that set the centre frequency are R3, R4 and R5 with C2, C3 and C5. R5 needs to be half the value of R3 and R4 and C3 needs to be twice the value of C2 and C4. R1 and R2 bias the op-amps to half the supply rail for linear operation. VR1 sets the depth of the null.

If C2 and C4 are 270pF and C3 is 540pF (2 x 270pF in parallel) and R3 and R4 are 10MΩ and R5 is 5MΩ (2 x 10MΩ in parallel) the centre frequency is about 60Hz (58.9Hz).

The formula to determine the centre frequency is:

$$F = \frac{1}{2\pi \, R3 \, C2} \quad \text{in Hertz,}$$

where
R3 = R4 and (R3) / 2 = R5
and
C2 = C4 and C2 + C4 = C3.

Both of the preceding circuits are derived from the 'Bridged-T' network.

2W audio amplifier

Where a low power audio amplifier is required operating on a supply voltage of 6 to 12V, the TBA820M is a good choice. This IC is an 8-pin DIL package and with a handful of components the amplifier can occupy very little space. The power output is dependent on the supply voltage and the loudspeaker impedance; higher supply voltages give more power as do a lower imped-ance speaker. The formula for power output is:

$$P_o \approx \frac{0.35 \times V^2}{R_L}$$

where P_o is the power output in watts
V^2 is the output voltage swing squared
R_L is the speaker impedance in ohms.

The output voltage swing will be approx 1 to 1.5V less for each portion of the output voltage centred on the half supply rail bias point due to the saturation voltage of the push-pull stage. For a supply voltage of 9V the best we can expect is about (9 - 3) = 6V peak-peak. This is an rms voltage of approx 2V. With 2V rms output the power is 0.55W in 8Ω and 1.1W in 4Ω.

For a supply voltage of 12V and 8Ω speaker impedance the maximum power output for the TBA820M is 2W, with a supply voltage of 9V and 8Ω speaker the power output is 1.2W. These figures are for an audio distortion figure of 10%, for greater fidelity the power output will be slightly less. The 8-pin DIL package does not have very good heatsinking so the 2W output should be considered the maximum safe limit.

The input signal is controlled by the volume control VR1. Capacitor C3 is an optional component where better ripple rejection is required, for

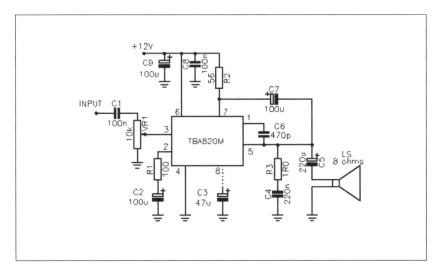

Fig 2.4. Audio amplifier using the TBA820M

most applications it can be omitted. Capacitor C4 and resistor R3 form a high frequency stabilising filter - a 'Zobel network'. Capacitor C6 sets the high frequency roll off; with the value shown the upper frequency response is about 15kHz. Increasing this value to 680pF lowers the cut off to about 8kHz.

The gain is determined by the value of R1, a lower value increases the closed loop gain. With the value shown the gain is approx 40dB. R1 and C6 inter-react to some extent, so the values shown should be adhered to for best performance. C7 sets the lower frequency cut off; with the values shown the response is about 20Hz. The TBA820M was a common choice for Walkman audio devices operating on 6V to drive a pair of headphones or a cassette recorder to drive the 8Ω speaker.

10W audio amplifier

This amplifier is designed for the normal automotive supply voltage of 10 to 16V and will make a good speaker driver for a mobile radio. One application could be to drive an external speaker for a handheld radio. The device is the TDA-2003, which is found in many car radios. The device is a TO-220 package with 5-pins and the tab is internally connected to the ground terminal (pin 3) so the heatsinking is simple. For maximum power output the speaker impedance needs to be 4Ω.

The input signal must be via a DC blocking capacitor to prevent upsetting the biasing. Resistors R2 and R3 set the closed loop gain, for less gain lower the value of R2. The networks R1 and C4 and C5 set the upper and lower frequency response. With the values shown the lower frequency cut off is approx 30Hz and the upper is approx 15kHz. R4 and C6 form the high frequency stability Zobel network.

The TDA-2003 is in essence an op-amp with an output stage that can drive up to 3.5A into a load. There is another IC in the same series

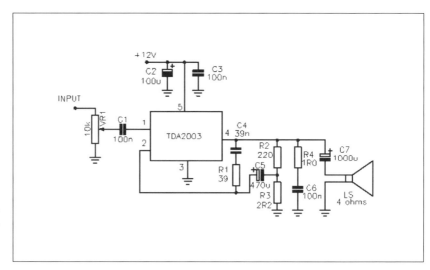

Fig 2.5. 10W audio amplifier using the TDA2003

designed as a DC driver but in reality it is only a selected version of the TDA-2003, as I discovered when comparing the two. The TDA-2003 is a very versatile device as it is DC coupled throughout and hence the frequency response extends down to DC. It can be used as a servo motor driver with thermal protection; back EMF and load dump transients all built in. The device will safely withstand up to +40V supply voltage transients, as it is an automotive grade device. If the supply voltage exceeds 40V the IC shuts down until the supply returns to normal. It can also be used as a 3A power supply regulator with suitable modification of the components.

Audio level monitoring circuit

In broadcast and recording studios the operators use a special type of audio level meter to ensure the level is correct. If the level is advanced too much the transmitter will over modulate, causing distortion. The meter used for this application is known as a 'Peak Programme Meter' (PPM). The audio signal is rectified and a weighting factor to the damping is used to make the meter needle hang at the last peak signal for a short time. The decay time of the hang circuit is adjusted to suit the type of signal, either speech or music. Peak Program Meters are expensive to purchase but we can make something almost as good with a couple of low cost integrated circuits and a few light-emitting diodes to replace the meter movement.

There are many uses for a peak program meter. If you are involved in relaying bulletins from one radio to another then a unit like this will enable you to monitor accurately the signal level being sent to the transmitter. It can also be used if telephone patching is used.

The circuit functions as a half wave rectifier with a peak hold. The diodes can be 1N4148 or 1N914 silicon diodes. The capacitor used for C2 needs to be a low leakage type such as a polycarbonate or polyester. The decay time for the signal is set by the value of R5. With the values shown the decay time is approx 0.1s. If the decay time needs to be made longer then increase the value of R5 rather than C2. The time to charge up the hang capacitor C2 is a function of the value and the output impedance of

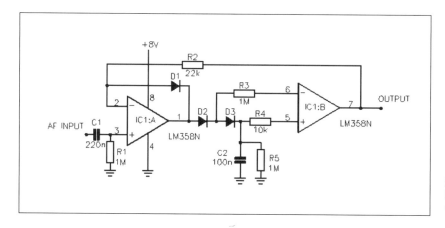

Fig 2.6. Peak Program Meter detector circuit

21

IC1A, which is quite high, so we cannot make C2 too large or we will not see the instantaneous peak of the audio signal.

The output signal is a DC voltage corresponding to the peak AC signal, for a pure sine wave input the DC voltage will be 1.414 times the rms input. This can either by displayed by a moving coil meter or a bar graph display. The bar graph display is preferred because all moving coil meters are heavily damped and cannot follow a rapidly changing signal. This inherently does not affect a bar graph.

The ubiquitous bar graph display is the National Semiconductors LM-3914 that can drive up to 10 LEDs and can be configured to operate in bar graph or dot mode. The LM-3914 requires very few components to make a working display. Two resistors are used to set the internal reference voltage; this can be any value between 1.25V to the full supply voltage. These resistors also set the LED current and hence the brightness. Pin 9 is either connected to the supply voltage to select the bar graph mode or left open circuit to select the dot mode.

The output voltage for the LED comparator divider chain is:

$$V_{out} = V_{ref} \times 1 + \frac{R2}{R1}$$

where V_{ref} = 1.25V.

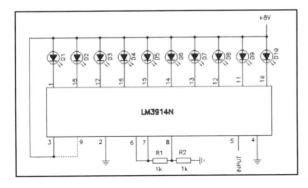

Fig 2.7. Basic LM-3914 display circuit

In the diagram of **Fig 2.7** the voltage is selected to be 2.5V full scale. If 1.25V is required, ground pin 8 and omit R2 and connect the bottom of R1 to ground. Pin 6 is the input to the reference voltage divider chain for the LED comparator and should be connected to pin 7.

The LEDs are lit in sequence from left to right as the voltage increases. LED D1 is connected to pin 1 and LED D10 is connected to pin 10, a clever bit of IC design by National Semiconductors when the IC was laid out. Unfortunately the other LEDs do not follow the same logic and you need to be careful when connecting these up. When the input signal is the same value as the reference voltage LED D10 will light. Hence, with the reference selected as 1.25V the LEDs will indicate 125mV increments. If a comparison voltage of less than 1.25V is required, the output from pin 7 can be divided down before passing it to pin 6. If an off set is required, say starting at 1V instead of zero volts, pin 4 can be used as this is the bottom of the resistor divider chain for the internal comparators that turn on the LEDs. Normally pin 4 is grounded but by feeding in a voltage here or inserting an appropriate resistor to develop the correct voltage we can introduce an off set voltage. The internal voltage divider consists of

10 1kΩ resistors connected in series. The LM-3914 data sheet contains more information on how to do this.

This display circuit is not limited to audio. It can be used as the basis of a peak reading RF wattmeter by applying the through line wattmeter detector diode DC signal to the peak hold rectifier circuit and the display bar graph. If the DC signal is less than 1.25V, adding an op-amp DC gain stage will increase the signal to the desired level. A good op-amp to choose is the Signetics NE-5534; this is a low noise version of the LM741 and features higher input impedance and lower operating current. The pin out is the same as the 741.

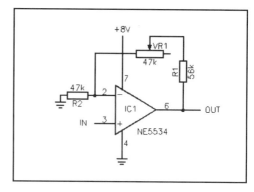

Fig 2.8. Basic DC non-inverting amplifier using an op-amp

The gain is the ratio of the resistors between the output and the input on pin 2 and the input resistor to ground on pin 2. With the values shown the gain is adjustable from about 2.2 to 3.2 times.

The formula for the DC gain is:

$$\text{Gain} = 1 + \frac{R1 + VR1}{R2}$$

Hence, when R1 + VR1 = R2 the gain is 2. It is normally not recommended that a gain of less than 2 be used for stability reasons. The input range is from zero volts up to supply. The maximum output voltage is approx the supply voltage minus 1.5V, so with an 8V supply we can swing the output up to about 6.5V.

Wideband white noise generator

Often when designing audio filters or amplifiers it is useful to have a source of wideband white noise. An application could be a graphic equaliser where it is tedious to sweep a sine wave audio oscillator across the band of interest to see the frequency response. By driving the graphic equaliser with a constant level white noise source we can excite all the frequencies at the same time and hence hear the effect each section has on the frequency response.

Fig 2.9. Wideband audio noise generator

The circuit shown in **Fig 2.9** is a simple wideband audio noise generator that generates a high output level into high impedance. Zener diode D1 generates wideband noise that is then amplified by TR1. The output level is approx 6V peak to peak. Capacitor C3 can be increased in value to limit the upper frequency range but this will reduce the output level considerably. With a 10nF capacitor the output drops to about 0.5V. Because the frequency response is shaped by C3 it isn't strictly a white noise source,

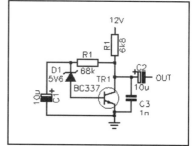

it's more like pink noise. With C1 at 1nF the frequency response is theoretically flat and the 3dB point is 147kHz. With C1 as 10nF the 3dB point is about 15kHz.

Simple audio oscillator

When we require a simple audio oscillator that needs to make a noise and the exact frequency and tone purity isn't of great concern, the circuit in **Fig 2.10** is about as simple as you can get. This is a relaxation oscillator using the inherent negative resistance region that all transistors exhibit. A more expensive version can be built using an uni-junction transistor but these today are scarce.

The frequency is a function of the value of the timing components; the inductance of LS and C1 but the supply voltage also causes the frequency to vary somewhat. If the application requires an alarm enunciator that needs to make a high noise level then this circuit is ideal as it occupies very little space. I call it the 'Squawk' oscillator because it sounds quite raucous, but it gets your attention. Definitely not the sort of oscillator for code practice!

The speaker is high impedance, the minimum impedance it will work with is about 50Ω and a 300Ω telephone earpiece is ideal because you can build the circuit on the back using the screw terminals as mounting points. You will need to experiment a bit to get the tone that best suits your application; you only have one component to vary, C1. The transistor type is quite uncritical: almost anything will work.

**Fig   2.10.
Squawk   audio
oscillator**

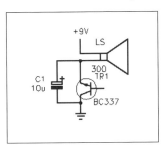

Tuning-up adapter

When tuning up a valve transmitter or linear amplifier we have a few adjustments to make. The anode tuning and loading controls need to be correctly set. If the antenna also uses an antenna tuning unit this is another set of controls to adjust. Combine the two together and we have a minimum of four controls to adjust. If the settings are made at low power, when we increase the drive level to maximum the adjustments need to be altered.

The usual method is first to get everything approximately correct at low power and then increase the drive to maximum and quickly retune all the controls. This places an undue stress on the valves and can lead to a shortening of their life. The operator is also stressed, because in the back of his mind is the need to do everything as quickly as possible, which can lead to mistakes with the consequences attached. Very few amateur high power linear amplifiers will withstand full carrier for any length of time. Not only are the valves unduly stressed but also the power supply components are being subjected to high dissipation under continuous carrier conditions.

What we need is a device that can drive the transmitter / linear amplifier to its full peak output power but doesn't overstress the valves due to

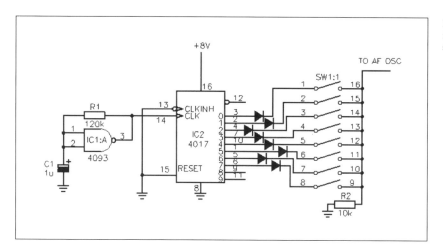

Fig 2.11. Tuning adapter logic section

excessive dissipation. Many of the valves used in linear amplifiers are not capable of continuous carrier output for more than a few seconds. They are OK when running SSB or Morse code as the average duty cycle is not more than 40%. If you have an electronic Morse code keyer, a simple solution is to set the keyer to about 50WPM and send short bursts of dots whilst making adjustments. This is a duty cycle of about 50% if the dot / space ratio is correct (sending a string of dashes is a duty cycle of about 75%).

Here is a tuning-up adapter that allows the transmitter to be driven to full output but the duty cycle can be varied from about 10% to 80%, so taking the stress off the valves. The circuits shown in **Fig 2.11** and **Fig 2.12** use low-cost components. It can be powered by a 9V transistor radio battery, as the current consumption is low. The circuit should be built into a well-screened enclosure to prevent RF from upsetting the electronics.

The logic section generates a square wave signal that corresponds to the duty cycle required. IC2 is a CD4017 decade counter with 10 outputs. A square wave oscillator built using a NAND gate (IC1A) clocks the counter. R1 and C1 set the clocking speed. The clock generates a signal that is equivalent to 12WPM Morse code. Eight of the outputs of IC2 are diode-OR-ed with the 8-pole DIP-switch SW1. The outputs of IC2 are clocked sequentially from the count of 0 to 9. First output 0 (pin 3) will go high for

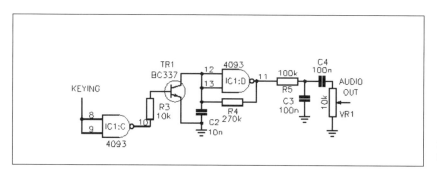

Fig 2.12. Keyed audio oscillator

one clock period and then fall low. As pin 3 returns to zero volts, pin 2 rises high and then low and so on. When the counter has counted up to 9 the cycle repeats again from output 0. The diodes are 1N914 or 1N4148 small signal diodes.

By closing switches in SW1 we can select how many of the eight outputs cause the transmitter to be turned on. If only one switch is closed the duty cycle is 1 in 10 (10%). If two switches are closed the duty cycle is 20%, etc. When all eight switches are closed the duty cycle is 80%. By selecting the number of switches to be closed we can drive the transmitter / linear to maximum peak power but with a long time period until the next pulse. A rotary switch can replace SW1.

The DC voltage appearing at the switch output is a representation of the transmitter 'On-Time' duty cycle. The DC signal is used to key an audio oscillator that is connected to the microphone input of the transmitter. This portion is shown in Fig 2.12.

The audio oscillator uses another gate from the CD4093 NAND gate IC. IC1D is a simple square wave oscillator that generates a 1kHz tone. The keying of IC1D is by TR1. The DC signal from the selector switch is inverted in IC1C and used to drive the transistor. When the logic generator output is low (no transmit pulse) the output of IC1C will be high, so turning on TR1. The collector of TR1 shorts out the input to IC1D and prevents the oscillator from running. When the input of IC1C is high, TR1 is turned off and the oscillator runs. The square wave audio signal is low pass filtered in R5 and C3 to turn it into a clean signal and VR1 sets the output level to the microphone amplifier.

If the transmitter is a CW type, there is no requirement for an audio tone and the keying can be taken directly from the logic switch and used to drive a suitable keying transistor.

Note: if the RF power meter used is not a peak reading type, the operator needs to be aware of the power that will be indicated using a normal through-line average reading wattmeter. When 10% duty cycle is selected the average power measured will be 10% of the peak power. When 80% duty cycle is selected the average power measured will be 80% of the peak power. A far better method is to use a peak reading wattmeter. Irrespective of the duty cycle selected, the peak reading wattmeter will always display the true peak power. Hence, a very low duty cycle can be used to tune up.

Gain controlled audio amplifier

Transmitters using AM, FM or SSB need a microphone amplifier that can be gain controlled to prevent over modulation. Some techniques are clipping or limiting stages but these generate harmonics of the audio waveform and degrade the speech quality. Where the audio distortion needs to be low, an automatic gain control method is the best option. The circuit shown in **Fig 2.13** uses a trio of NPN transistors with a novel method of controlling the output amplitude.

TR1 to TR3 are small signal NPN transistors such as BC337 etc. TR1 and TR2 are configured as a differential pair, with TR3 controlling the current flowing in TR2. TR1 is AC coupled to the output. The input signal on the base of TR3 is the bottom transistor in a cascode pair. The control voltage is derived from a rectified signal from the following audio stages where sufficient amplitude is available to drive a rectifier diode, or it could be a manually set voltage. When TR1 is turned on, the output signal is shunted to ground so reducing the output level. TR1 and TR2 are operated in grounded base whereas TR3 is operated in grounded emitter. The voltage amplification of TR3 and TR2 is high.

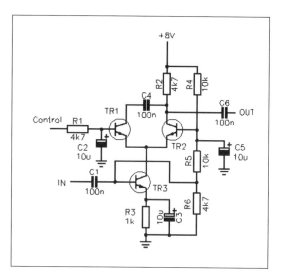

Fig 2.13. Gain controlled audio amplifier

The values of the coupling capacitors C1, C4 and C6 suit 'communications quality' speech with attenuation to the lower frequencies.

In an AM or SSB transmitter the best place to obtain the control voltage is from the rectified RF after the power amplifier stage. This will then *close the loop* between the microphone amplifier and the final output stage, so giving the best linearity.

Audio speech clipper and low-pass filter

This circuit is a low cost audio speech clipper and low-pass filter suitable for a simple transmitter. Whereas the audio quality is not as good as an AGC system as described above, when the emphasis is on intelligibility rather than quality this circuit performs well. It has been found by subjective listening tests on very weak signals that a certain amount of third and fifth harmonic distortion *increases* the intelligibility, although the signal sounds

Fig 2.14. Audio speech clipper and low-pass filter

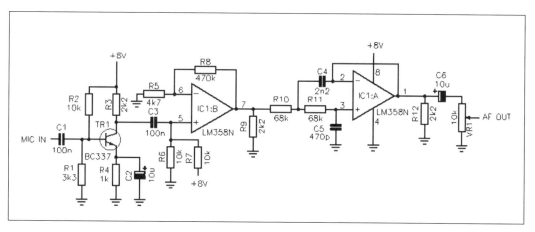

harsher when a strong signal is received. By shaping the audio response so the higher frequency components of the speech waveform are boosted and the lower frequency components are suppressed the intelligibility improves considerably. Communications speech quality is definitely not high fidelity!

Transistor TR1 is a medium gain amplifier stage suiting low to medium impedance microphones. This is coupled to an Op-Amp (IC1b) configured as a high gain audio amplifier. The feedback resistor R8 between the output and the inverting input and the shunt resistor R5 set the closed loop voltage gain to 100 times. For heavier clipping the value of R8 should be increased. (To reduce the higher frequency components further a small value capacitor can be shunted across R8 to roll off higher frequencies). R6 and R7 bias the first Op-Amp to half rail and this DC voltage appears at the output pin of the first stage. The second Op-Amp (IC1a) is DC coupled and is also biased to half rail.

When the input from the microphone exceeds a certain level, the first Op-Amp output swings rail to rail (up to within 1.5V of the supply rails) giving a clipped signal of constant amplitude. With a large input from the microphone this is a square wave of approx 5V p-p at the audio frequency, when a 8V supply is used. Because this clipped signal is rich in harmonics a low pass filter is used to reduce the harmonic content, leaving a near sinusoidal waveform. R10, R11, C4 and C5 set the cut off frequency of the low pass filter. With the values shown the cut off is approx 3kHz. R9 and R12 shunted across the outputs of the Op-Amp increase the bias current in the output stages and eliminate cross over distortion. If using an Op-Amp other than the LM158 series these may not be required. The audio level to the transmitter modulator is set by VR1.

The values of the input coupling capacitors (C1 and C3) set the low frequency roll off, increasing the values will lower the cut off frequency to low audio frequencies in the speech signal.

CHAPTER 3

Metering, display and control circuits

In this chapter:

- Rotator or elevator readout display
- A voltage indicator and alarm circuit
- Mains frequency monitor
- A simple battery voltage display
- Sequencer circuit
- Relay speed-up circuit
- Inrush current limiter for low voltage power supplies
- Inrush current limiter for high voltage supplies
- Metering high voltage supplies
- Electronic thermometer and over temperature alarm
- Temperature controlled crystal oven
- Triode valve cathode stabiliser
- 'El Cheapo' beam indicator
- Latching relay control circuit
- Alternative latching relay circuit
- Variable duty cycle oscillator
- Liquid level monitor

FOR THOSE amateurs who are bit inclined mechanically but limited in the electronics field we start this chapter with a simple rotator or elevator display circuit that gives reasonable accuracy. The circuit is based on the National Semiconductors LM-3914 to drive 10 LEDs to indicate the position of the antenna.

Rotator or elevator readout display

The rotator or elevator is coupled to a linear potentiometer by suitable gearing so that it makes one complete rotation corresponding to either 360° or 90° rotation depending on the application. The LM-3914 is operated in the

Fig 3.1. An an-
tenna rotator or
elevator display

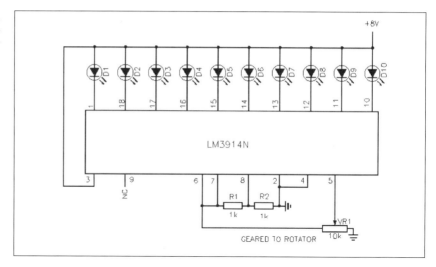

dot-mode by leaving pin 9 open circuit.

The description will focus on the rotator application; the elevator application should be clear from this description. When the antenna is turned to North the output voltage from the pot is half the maximum. The 10 LEDs are arranged in a compass circle with the fifth LED positioned at the point designated as North. When the antenna is turned so that the antenna points due South, the voltage will be either zero volts or maximum, in this case 2.5V because of the reference voltage resistors R1 and R2. Each LED corresponds to 36° when used as a rotator or 9° when used for an elevator. Although this is quite coarse with a small Yagi antenna the beamwidth will be more than this so there is no need for any better accuracy. If the antenna is less than a 10-element Yagi the beamwidth at 3dB points will be greater than 30°.

If a standard 270° rotation pot is used for the elevator, which only traverses 90°, a DC gain amplifier with a gain of 3 can be used to amplify the pot output voltage up to the required amount (see chapter 2 for a suitable circuit). Alternatively, gearing up the elevator rotation by 3:1 will achieve the same result. The electronic method is by far the easier method. Mechanically adjusting the pot to bring the output voltage to zero or maximum at each end of the travel is all that is required to set up the calibration. For the elevator the simplest method is to attach a short pendulum with a weight attached to the pot shaft so that it hangs down vertically. Using Newton's gravity this will cause the pot shaft to rotate as the antenna is elevated.

A voltage indicator and alarm circuit

For monitoring a power supply output voltage a moving coil meter is the traditional method. But moving coil meters today are expensive and occupy considerable front panel space. We can use a bar graph display for an indicator, as we don't normally need to know the voltage to the nearest mV.

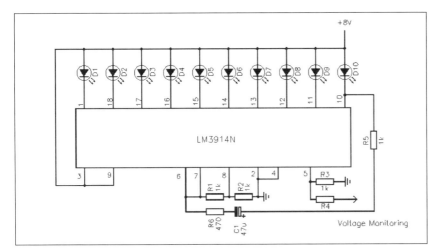

Fig 3.2. Output
voltage monitor
and alarm cir-
cuit

Also it is useful if the indicator can give us an alert if the voltage is too high. The LM-3914 can do both of these and with 10 LEDs gives a reasonably accurate indication.

The voltage to be monitored is divided down by R4 and R3 so that the normal output voltage causes seven LEDs to be lit. If the output voltage increases so that LED 10 is lit, the LM-3914 will flash the entire bar graph, thus alerting the user. The rate of flashing is set by the value of C1 and R5. By moving the resistor R5 to another LED it will cause the display to flash when that LED is lit. To operate in bar graph mode pin 9 must be connected to the supply rail.

Mains frequency monitor

The frequency of the public mains supply varies about the nominal frequency of 50Hz. This circuit uses another National Semiconductors integrated circuit, which is a *Frequency to Voltage* converter. This is the LM-2907 and it is a very versatile IC with lots of applications. Although this application is to monitor the mains frequency, the same principle can be used for other low frequencies, such as CTCSS tones of 67Hz to 250.3Hz. It can also be used to make an accurate tachometer for internal combustion engines by measuring the number of ignition pulses.

The circuit uses the 14-pin DIL version, the LM-2907N. There is another version that only has eight pins but this limits the usefulness, as some of the internal connection points are not accessible on the eight-pin package. On the 14-pin DIL package pins 6, 7, 13 and 14 are not connected and should be left floating.

The frequency to voltage converter is supplied with an AC signal derived from a low voltage transformer that is also used to supply the regulated 8V that the LM-2907 requires.

The LM-2907 uses a differential input amplifier between pins 1 and 11. For a single ended input such as we are using we have to AC ground

Fig 3.3. Frequency to voltage converter

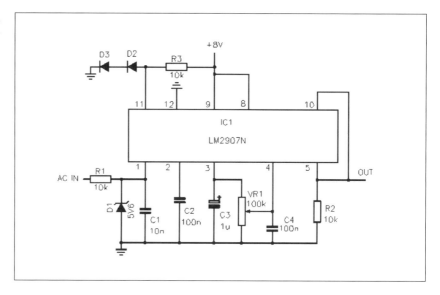

one of the inputs. Here pin 1 is used and pin 11 is supplied with a reference voltage of about 1.4V by diodes D2 and D3 (1N914 or 1N 4148). The AC signal is clamped by D1 to 5.6V positive and 0.6V negative, D1 only needs to be a 500mW zener. Hence, every time the voltage on pin 1 crosses +1.4V the input will toggle. C1 prevents spurious spikes upsetting the input stage. The input amplifier drives a *flip-flop* circuit with positive feedback to generate a truncated (flat-topped) triangular wave of an exact voltage peak. The value of the capacitor on pin 2 determines the ramp slope and hence the peak voltage. This is then applied to a *charge-pump* circuit that charges up an external capacitor and resistor network connected between pin 3 to ground. The DC voltage appearing across C3 / VR1 is directly proportional to the input frequency. The decay time is determined by VR1. The voltage is then applied to an Op-amp voltage follower stage connected between pins 4 and 5 with feedback from pin 10. This voltage can be used to drive a moving coil meter or some other type of display.

The formula to derive the output voltage is:

$$V_{out} = V_{cc} \times F_{in} \times R_3 \times C_2 \times K$$

where V_{cc} is the supply voltage (hence it must be a stable voltage),
F_{in} is the input signal frequency in Hertz,
R_3 and C_2 are the timing components connected to pin 2 and 3 (C2 and VR1),
K is a gain constant, typically 1.0.

With the values shown the circuit outputs the following voltages:
45Hz = 3.6V
50Hz = 4.0V
55Hz = 4.4V.

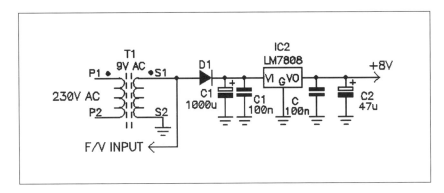

Fig 3.4. Power
supply details

The preset resistor VR1 allows calibration to a known frequency signal.

The converter requires a good stabilised supply and the circuit shown in **Fig 3.4** does everything needed. The transformer T1 should have a 6V to 9V AC secondary with at least a 2VA rating. The input signal to the LM-2907 is taken from the secondary winding before the half wave rectifier diode D1. D1 is a 1N4002 or similar 50V / 1A diode.

The display can be an LM-3914 set for dot mode with the reference voltage set to about 4.5V. However, this will give a very cramped reading and a better method is to expand the reference voltage so that mid scale corresponds to 4.0V and the bottom LED is lit when 3.6V is applied and the top LED is lit when 4.4V is applied. This gives a resolution of 1Hz per step. Because we have a preset pot VR1 in the output of the LM-2907 circuit means we can choose a more suitable voltage that will allow the use of E12 range resistors for the reference voltage setting.

The bottom of the internal resistor divider chain terminating at pin 4 is supplied with a stable 3.3V voltage derived from zener D11 (500mW) and R3 from the +8V supply. Because the voltage is 3.3V and not the required 3.6V we need to shift the upper reference voltage down by a similar amount to 4.1V. Using E12 resistor values we find that with a 1kΩ and a 2k2Ω resistor we get a voltage of 4.0V which is 0.1V lower than desired. But because we have the preset on the LM-2907 we can set the display to mid scale when an accurate 50Hz signal is injected.

By changing the upper and lower reference voltages the scale can be expanded to cover just 5Hz. This will then gives a display with ±2.5Hz either side of the centre frequency corresponding to 0.5Hz per step.

Fig 3.5. Modification to the LM-3914 to expand the scale

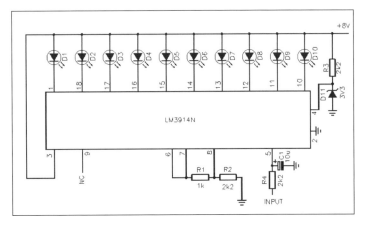

33

This would be a useful addition for portable generators for standby power operation or contest operation.

A simple battery voltage display

When we need a simple circuit to monitor a voltage but do not need as many as the 10 LEDs that the LM-3914 uses, a solution is to use a few voltage comparators. By setting the reference voltage to two comparators we can display under, over and nominal voltage. A use for this might be a quick indication of whether the battery voltage for a handheld piece of equipment was satisfactory.

The basis of the circuit is shown in **Fig 3.6**.

Two voltage comparators are connected with a voltage divider chain from the battery voltage and when the battery voltage is above the nominal voltage the green LED is lit. If the voltage is below the nominal voltage the red LED will be lit. The comparators are an LM-393N, which is a dual comparator IC. The reference voltage is supplied by the 3.9V zener that is a 500mW type. The input voltage from the 9V battery is divided down to half the supply voltage. Hence, the trip point is 7.8V. If the battery voltage is greater than this the green LED signifies the battery is OK and if the voltage is below 7.8V the red LED tells the user the battery is no longer satisfactory. If the battery voltage is exactly 7.8V both LEDs will be lit. A small 'push-test' switch can be used to switch on the circuit when the battery voltage needs to be checked. By the addition of a load resistor (RL) to suit the battery type this can make a handy battery checker.

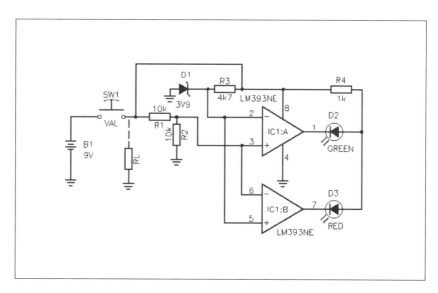

Fig 3.6. Battery voltage display

Sequencer circuit

For those amateurs operating on VHF / UHF using a high power linear amplifier and a masthead mounted low noise amplifier (LNA) the use of a circuit to sequence correctly the various items is essential. Simply connecting the PTT output of the transceiver to the linear amplifier and the LNA control line will usually lead to expensive problems. The danger always exists that a large amount of RF power can be driven into the output of the LNA if the coaxial relays do not change over quickly enough or in the correct order. The operate time for a typical RF coaxial relay is about 15 to 25ms and the time to finish contact bounce can be as much again. So if any RF power is applied before about 50ms there is a good chance of some damage occurring.

Taking the moment in time where the operator presses the microphone PTT, things should happen in this order:

1. Low noise amplifier is switched off and the antenna change over relay switches from receive to transmit
2. Linear amplifier biasing circuits are enabled so that the amplifier becomes active
3. Transceiver is keyed and transmission may begin.

Many transceivers when first keyed up generate a burst of RF power. If the linear is also keyed by the same line as the transceiver, it can cause a large burst of RF power to be sent from the linear amplifier before the coaxial relays have finished opening or closing to send the RF to the antenna. In many cases the relay contacts will be somewhere in mid travel when this occurs and either the relay contacts will be damaged by arcing or the power is sent into the back end of the LNA. This will destroy it very quickly.

When the transmission is completed we need to return to receive in a controlled manner the opposite of the receive to transmit case. So the steps are:

1. Switch off transceiver PTT
2. Switch off the linear PTT
3. Switch on the LNA and change over relays.

This is what a correctly designed *sequencer circuit* performs. The time delay between each step can be short, the whole receive to transmit process taking about 0.5s for average relays. The circuit shown in **Fig 3.7** achieves this with two low cost op-amps and a handful of components. In my 2m and 6m transceivers the sequencer is constructed on a small board that easily fits inside the average transceiver and is powered from a convenient existing internal +9V supply rail and the +12V main supply rail. The supply can be almost any voltage from about 6V to 15V and the current drawn is very small, about 20mA in total. In the case of the 70cm trans-

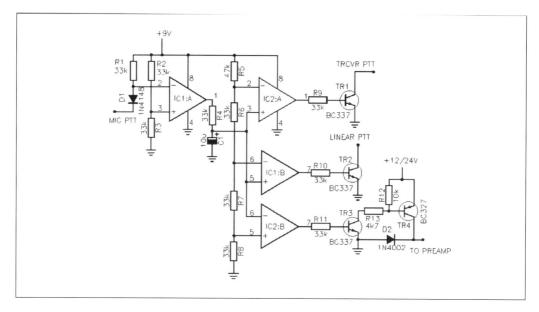

Fig 3.7. Sequencer circuit for linear amplifier and masthead mounted LNA

ceiver there is insufficient room to mount even a small board and so the sequencer is contained in a small die cast box and wired to the transceiver. The box contains connectors for the linear PTT and the masthead LNA control lines. 12V is tapped off from the transceiver and used to power the sequencer. A printed circuit board is used and it measures 35 x 35mm so the circuit is quite small. With SMD components the board can be shrunk to 15 x 15mm.

The circuit uses two LM-358N dual op-amps to control the switching. We could have used voltage comparators but op-amps do the job just as well at these slow switching speeds and cost a little less. If you are feeling masochistic, a single LM324 quad op-amp will also do the job, but I find the pin out of the LM324 a nightmare to work with. In any case two LM358s cost less than an LM324.

IC1A is the interface between the transceiver PTT and the rest of the

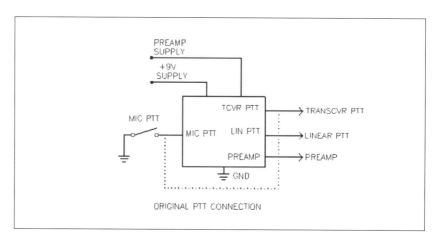

Fig 3.8. Connection details

circuitry. The PTT wire from the microphone must be disconnected and routed to the sequencer. The TCVR PTT line from the sequencer returns to the transceiver to do the transceiver switching. See **Fig 3.8** for connection details.

When the microphone PTT is keyed the output of IC1A goes high and starts to charge C1 via R4. The time constant of R4 and C1 determines the speed of the sequencer switching. With the values shown it is about 330ms. To increase the switching time, increase the value of R4. When the voltage on C1 rises to the trip point of the bottom comparator (IC2B) the output of this IC switches off and so the preamp supply voltage is also switched off. The preamp supply voltage also powers the coaxial antenna relay mounted at the masthead. Hence, the coaxial relay is energised for receive and switched off for transmit. This only requires one wire from the masthead to the sequencer. I normally use 'line powering' for masthead mounted LNAs so the receive downlead carries the LNA supply voltage and the relay uses the same voltage. This is arranged for by using 'bias-tees' to isolate the RF and DC signals.

Note that the inverting and non-inverting inputs for IC2B differ to the other comparators because we need IC2B to switch off, whereas the other two comparators need to switch *on* as the voltage across C1 rises to maximum.

The next comparator to trip is IC1B, which switches on the linear PTT. Finally comparator IC2A trips and sends the transceiver PTT ground back to the transceiver to make it switch from receive to transmit.

When the microphone PTT is released, the reverse sequence happens as C1 discharges to zero through R4 because the output of IC1A is now pulled to ground.

Relay speed-up circuit

Many relays are a bit slow to switch. One way of speeding up the closure of the contacts is to apply a higher DC voltage. If we double the DC supply voltage most relays will close in approx 50% of the time, compared with the normal operating voltage. However, using double the supply voltage will cause the relay to draw excessive current and it may burn out. The circuit shown in **Fig 3.9** overcomes this problem by limiting the current after the relay has been energised.

The circuit consists of a simple DC voltage doubler built around an op-amp. If you are perceptive you will recognise the oscillator as that used for the Morse code oscillator in chapter 2. The oscillator runs at about 5kHz

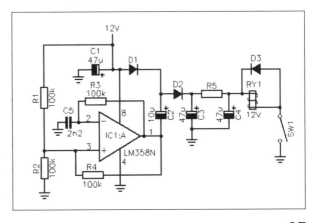

Fig 3.9. Relay speed-up circuit

and pumps up the 12V supply by almost the same figure. So the voltage appearing at the output across C3 is nearly 24V. The resistor R5 between C3 and C4 needs to be approximately the same value as the relay coil resistance and rated for adequate power. For most applications a 2W resistor will be OK. When SW1 is open the voltage across C4 is charged to approx 24V. When the switch is closed, because of the 24V stored in C4, this causes the sudden rush of current that pulls in the relay quickly and the voltage falls to around 12V because of the voltage drop in R5.

The diodes used for D1 and D2 can be 1A Schottky types for the lowest forward voltage but at 5kHz we can use almost any silicon diode; the 1N4002 works well in this circuit. The voltage rating of C3 and C4 should be 35V and C2 can be a 25V type. D3 can be a 1N4002 to clamp the back EMF spike when the relay is turned off. Note: This circuit can only supply about 100mA maximum, so the relay coil resistance should not be less than about 120Ω. A common UHF antenna change over relay for 12V is the Magnetic Devices MD-951 rated at 50W RF at up to 470MHz, this relay has a 170Ω coil and will draw approx 70mA when operated on 12V.

For applications where one side of the relay is connected to ground, **Fig 3.10** can be used.

TR1 can be a BC327 or 2N2907 and R6 and R7 can be 10kΩ and 4k7Ω respectively.

For applications requiring more current, see chapter 4 covering power supplies, where a simple 'boost converter' is detailed that can supply up to 1A at 24V.

Fig 3.10. Circuit for relay with one terminal grounded

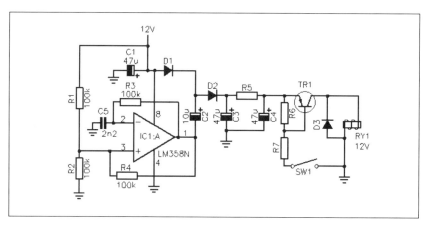

Inrush current limiter for low voltage power supplies

Switching a large transformer on with a simple mains on / off switch is not a clever idea. If you are unlucky and catch the mains cycle at or near the peak the transformer makes some interesting noises. If you have ever wondered what makes that *'thwung'* noise, it is the laminations, windings and the metal lid of the power supply reacting to the sudden jolt it gets when you hit the on / off switch near the peak of the mains cycle. This puts the transformer windings, the rectifier diodes and the smoothing capacitors under a lot of stress. In high voltage supplies you can see lots of *'magic smoke'* when something lets go due to the severe stress the components are subjected to. It also causes the contacts of the main on / off switch to burn away due to the highly inductive current that is generated.

What we need is a simple circuit to limit the inrush current until the output voltage has risen to near full output. A simple method is to place a low resistance in series with the mains and then switch it out when the output voltage has risen to about two-thirds of the nominal. This is commonly known as a *'soft start'* circuit.

Fig 3.11 shows the components that are used in the input circuit. The current limiting resistor is switched into circuit when the main on / off switch SW1 is first turned on. The value of R1 should be chosen to limit the inrush current to something sensible, with 12Ω and a 230V AC supply the inrush current is limited to about 20A. The power rating of R1 also needs to be considered, a 10 to 20W wire-wound resistor is normally adequate.

When the output voltage has risen to about two-thirds of the nominal the relay contact RY1 is used to short out the resistor. This circuit is inserted between the main on / off switch SW1 and the transformer primary. The circuit that controls the switching of RY1 is a voltage detector shown in **Fig 3.12**.

The voltage detector is connected to the output of the power supply. When the main on / off switch is closed the output voltage will slowly rise until the voltage exceeds the zener voltage. When this occurs, TR1 will turn on and hence TR2, which supplies 12V to the relay RY1 and this causes the contact to close and supply full mains voltage to the transformer. The time it takes will be approximately half a second.

Scientists and engineers have puzzled for years about the magic ingredient that makes semiconductors work. We can now reveal the secret, it is smoke. You will find that when a semiconductor fails it emits this 'Magic Smoke' and so far scientists or engineers have not established a way to replace the smoke to make the device work again.

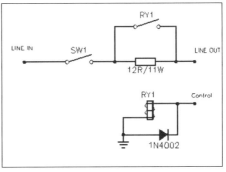

Fig 3.11. Inrush current limiter

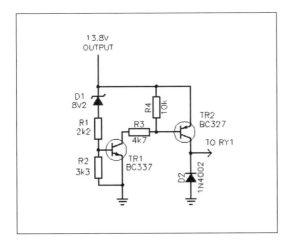

Fig 3.12. Control circuit for relay

Inrush current limiter for high voltage supplies

For high voltage supplies, such as those used to supply the anode voltage of a linear amplifier, the circuit in Fig 3.12 can be modified to monitor the voltage appearing across the bottom smoothing capacitor in the high voltage reservoir bank.

Normally the smoothing capacitor bank consists of several high voltage electrolytics connected in series to obtain the required working voltage. A supply of about 2kV might use 6 x 450V capacitors connected in series with sharing resistors across each capacitor to ensure each capacitor has an equal voltage across it. The voltage appearing across the bottom capacitor is hence one sixth of the anode voltage. The voltage occurring when the supply is at 2kV is hence 2000/6 = 333V. If the zener is selected to conduct when about 250V appears across the bottom capacitor, the relay will be pulled in at any voltage above 250V.

The modified circuit is shown in **Fig 3.13**. The zener diode used for D1 should be adequately rated and a good option is to make the required voltage up from several 1W zeners connected in series, say 5 x 47V / 1W zeners. Resistor R1 needs to be a minimum of 2W. C1 introduces some filtering and adds a further small delay before the transistors switch the relay on. The circuit is powered from an auxiliary 12V supply rail that is used to switch the other relays in the linear amplifier and is derived from the main transformer with a low voltage winding. This low voltage supply and the circuit in Fig 3.12 could have been used to remotely detect the HV, but monitoring the HV directly is a better option.

Fig 3.13. High voltage monitor and relay driver circuit

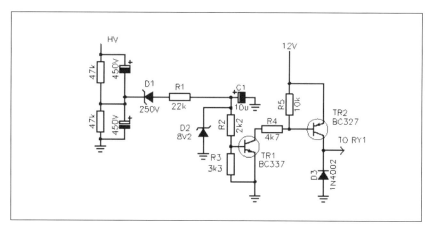

Metering high voltage supplies

A linear amplifier using a valve requires a high anode voltage, perhaps as much as 3kV. In order to measure levels like this we need to exercise extreme caution because of the lethal voltages involved. A good method is to measure the voltage appearing across the bottom smoothing capacitor and use this as an indication of the total anode voltage. With six capacitors connected in series the voltage appearing across the bottom capacitor will be a sixth of the total. If we divide the voltage with suitable scaling resistors we can then use a low voltage meter to indicate the anode voltage.

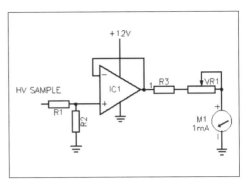

Fig 3.14 shows a method of performing voltage measurement to drive a 1mA moving coil meter. The meter scale can be modified with *Letraset* to give the correct full-scale voltage.

Fig 3.14. High voltage metering circuit

Resistors R1 and R2 are used to scale the voltage appearing across the bottom smoothing capacitor to some low voltage, perhaps 5V. The IC can be almost any single supply rail op-amp. The op-amp is configured as a unity gain voltage follower and the resistors connected to the output allow the full-scale deflection of the 1mA meter to be set.

The output of IC1 can also be connected to an under-voltage detector that will lock out the power supply if a serious under-voltage condition occurs, possibly a shorted valve or other component.

Electronic thermometer and over temperature alarm

Temperature monitoring is often required. An example might be the exhaust air temperature of a valve linear amplifier, or the water temperature of a water-cooled valve. If the temperature rises above a certain level an indicator warns the operator of the problem. There are many ways of measuring temperature accurately. Devices we can use are negative temperature coefficient thermistors (NTC), semiconductor junctions or custom ICs designed for this task. Of the many ways, the custom IC offers the simplest solution because the device is calibrated to a high degree of accuracy. The circuit shown in **Fig 3.15** measures the air temperature and switches on an LED if the temperature exceeds the set point.

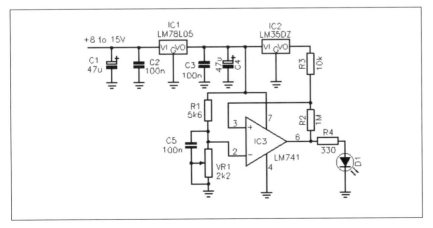

Fig 3.15. Over temperature alarm circuit

The circuit uses the National Semiconductors LM35 temperature measuring IC. The LM35 is the Celsius version and the LM34 is the Fahrenheit version. The LM35 is calibrated during manufacture to produce an accurate output voltage of +10mV/°C over the range of 0 to +150°C. Hence, the output voltage when the temperature is +100°C is exactly 1.00V. The accuracy of the output voltage at +25°C is such that typically an uncertainty of only ±0.5°C occurs when the voltage is measured.

The LM35 is available in several different packages. For our application we can select the lowest cost one, which is in the three-pin TO-92 plastic package (suffix Z). For those applications not requiring the ultimate in accuracy instead of using the tighter specification LM35C we can choose the slightly looser specification version, the LM35DZ.

The LM35 requires a minimum supply voltage of 4V and will work safely with a supply voltage of up to 20V. For our application we will choose the popular 5V supply and use a low current voltage regulator to power the LM35 and also provide the stable reference voltage required for the voltage sensing circuit.

The LM35 temperature sensor IC supplies a voltage to the op-amp IC3 configured as a voltage comparator. The threshold of the comparator is set by VR1. With the values shown the maximum temperature is approx +140°C. When the output of the LM35 equals or exceeds the threshold voltage set by VR1 the LED will light.

The LM35 should be mounted close to the air temperature to be monitored and bonded to a small piece of metal to act as a thermal mass. If measuring the exhaust temperature of a linear amplifier, the LM35 should be connected by wires twisted together and suitable RF decoupling capacitors connected between the input and output to ground to prevent stray RF from upsetting the measurement.

To set up the circuit, connect a DVM between the reference input of IC3 (pin 2) and ground and adjust VR1 to obtain the correct threshold voltage. For example, for +60°C the voltage required is 0.6V.

Temperature controlled crystal oven

When operating on the higher UHF and microwave bands the frequency stability of the crystal oscillator becomes a problem. Although we may have purchased the best stability crystal, if the ambient temperature within the equipment varies over a wide range the oscillator may still drift an unacceptable amount. The simplest way to get around the problem is to hold the crystal at a stable elevated temperature such as +70°C. This is the basis of an OCXO (*oven controlled crystal oscillator*).

The circuit shown in **Fig 3.16** is a variation of the previous use of the LM35 and controls a heating element to hold the crystal at a stable temperature. The heating element is a low value 2W to 5W resistor that is switched on and off as the temperature varies. This type of control circuit is known as a *'Bang-Bang'* control because the heating element is either on

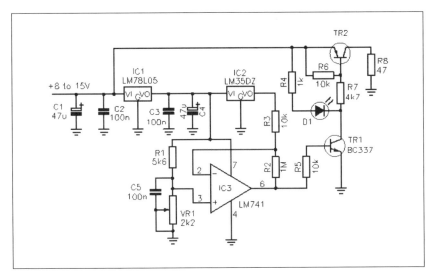

Fig 3.16. Crystal oven control circuit

or off and although not as accurate as a fully *proportional control* system it will still yield good results. By building in some thermal mass the rate of change of the crystal temperature is slow and the resulting drift is negligible. The time to raise the crystal from normal ambient temperature to the required +70°C when first switched on will largely depend on the heating element power and the thermal mass it has to raise. Once the crystal is at the required temperature the rate of change of temperature will be slow. The LM35 is bonded to one side of the crystal envelope and the heating element to the opposite side. Super glue can be used to attach the LM35; the heating element is attached thermally with a dab of heatsink compound between the resistor body and the crystal envelope. Heatsink compound can also be used to connect the LM35 plastic body to the crystal envelope. The crystal, heater and LM35 should be enclosed in a thermal jacket to prevent sudden changes of temperature. A small block of polystyrene foam with the centre hollowed out can be slipped over the components stopping any draughts from lowering the temperature.

The input connections to the voltage comparator are different to the ones used in Fig 3.15. This is because the heating element needs to be switched on at low temperatures and switched off when the LM35 output voltage equals or exceeds the set point. The resistor value used for the heating element (R8) will determine how quickly the crystal reaches the set point temperature. With the value shown and a 12V supply the resistor will dissipate approx 3W. This value will have to be established empirically to get the optimum result. The transistor used for TR2 will also depend on the heating element current. For the value of R8 shown the heater current will be approx 250mA and so a transistor such as a 2N2907 or BC327 will be adequate. For higher currents a beefier device would be needed. LED D1 will be lit when the heater is on and serves as an indication to correct operation.

Temperature control: an unusual application

I built a variation of the circuit shown in Fig 3.16 some time ago for a friend who needed to incubate duck eggs and these needed to be held at a precisely controlled temperature within ±2°C. The output of TR2 was connected to a 12V relay coil and the relay contacts switched several 230V 40W lamps in the incubator. It was found that the control circuit held the air temperature within the polystyrene foam lined incubator box to within ±0.5°C of the desired.

Triode valve cathode stabiliser

Many triodes used for the UHF and microwave bands are designed to operate in grounded grid. When a triode is operated in grounded grid, the grid is directly grounded to the chassis and the cathode then needs to be lifted above ground by the voltage required to generate the correct biasing. This means we need a circuit that can be adjustable to set the correct idling current and also hold the cathode voltage constant as the anode current varies.

For a low power amplifier often selecting a suitable value zener to place in series with the cathode to ground will work. However, when the power output is more than a few watts this means we need a high power zener diode. When several triodes are paralleled to gain more power output the anode current can be several amperes on speech peaks.

Using valves such as the 2C39 family or the more powerful Russian triodes such as the Gi7bt often requires a cathode stabiliser that can handle 3A or more. If the mode is SSB then any variation of the biasing voltage when RF drive is applied will cause intermodulation distortion products to be generated. The circuit shown in **Fig 3.17** holds the cathode voltage within 50mV from a cathode current of 100mA to more than 5A.

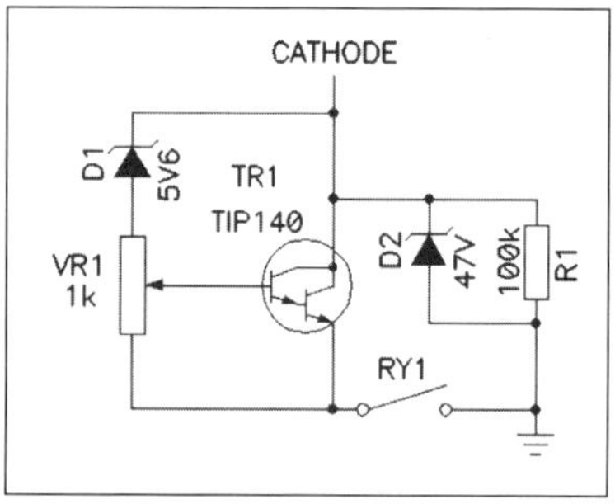

Fig 3.17. Cathode biasing regulator

The circuit is essentially a current boosted zener with an adjustable voltage. Zener diode D1 sets the reference voltage and this only needs to be a 500mW or 1W type. The current amplification is performed by TR1, which is a large NPN Darlington with a high current gain. The TIP140 shown has a minimum gain of approx 1000 at 5A collector current. The TIP140 is a bit of an overkill in this application, but was chosen due to its reasonable cost and the fact that it can withstand high peak current surges which can occur if the valve flashes over between anode to cathode.

Preset VR1 sets the cathode voltage to the required voltage. Zener diode D2 (1W) and resistor R1 (0.5W) serve to cut off the valve during standby periods. The value of D2 needs to be approx 10V more than the valve cut off voltage; in most cases a 47V / 1W zener will be satisfactory. R1 is fitted in case D2 should fail open circuit, possibly as the result of a flashover in the valve. The relay contact RY1 is controlled by the linear amplifier PTT and is open on standby and closed when transmitting. Cathode current metering can be inserted between RY1 and the ground point.

TR1 needs to be mounted on a good heatsink with an insulating washer to prevent shorting of the collector to ground. With a typical Gi7bt valve operating with an anode voltage of 2kV the cathode voltage is approx 25V to achieve 50mA of idle current. Under full drive the cathode current can peak to as much as 1A because of the added grid current. The power dissipation in the transistor will be 25W under this condition. The TIP140 is a Darlington with a maximum collector-emitter voltage of 60V, a peak collector current of 10A and a rated dissipation of 125W when properly heatsinked. Hence, it is not unduly stressed at this level.

'El Cheapo' beam indicator

This circuit was originally proposed by Roy Schofield, G3YCI, who was a member of the North Liverpool Radio Club, G3JQA, at a time when I also lived in Liverpool. Roy was licensed around the same time as me in the 1970s and Roy was a bright young electronics engineer studying for his degree at Liverpool University. The idea that prompted this was an article in Pat Hawker's, G3VA, 'Technical Topics' column in *RadCom* by G3KGA, which used a nine-wire multi-core cable to light one of eight lamps to indicate the position of the antenna.

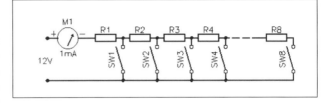

Fig 3.18. Simple beam position indicator

Roy put his thinking cap on and came up with a solution that only required a two-core cable and a cheap 1mA moving coil meter. Both systems use a number of reed switches and a bar magnet that closes a reed switch when the magnet is positioned over the reed switch. Hence, the resolution isn't great but can be improved by adding more switches and resistors. The original G3YCI design used eight reed switches but it can be expanded to 16 switches and so provide better resolution.

The eight reed switches are arranged in a circle with the common point being the negative rail. A bar magnet attached to an arm on the rotating mast sweeps over the reed switches as the antenna is rotated. The resistors are arranged such that the 1mA meter current increases as the antenna mast is turned. The values for the resistors are listed in **Table 3.1** below. The indicator requires a stable 12V supply that can be derived from a 12V zener diode, as the current drawn is only 1mA maximum.

When this was designed there was a massive amount of reed switches on the surplus market due to quality issues with the newer *Cross-Point* telephone exchanges and a handful could be bought for less than the price of a pint. In one of the new telephone exchange I visited during my term of office with the British Post Office, technicians were changing out of specification reed switches at the rate of a tea chest full a week!

8-reed system	16-reed system
R1 = 12k	R1 = 12k
R2 = 1k8	R2 = 820
R3 = 2k2	R3 = 910
R4 = 4k3	R4 = 1k
R5 = 4k7	R5 = 1k2
R6 = 8k2	R6 = 1k5
R7 = 16k	R7 = 1k8
R8 = 47k	R8 = 2k
	R9 = 2k7
	R10 = 3k3
	R11 = 4k7
	R12 = 6k2
	R13 = 10k
	R14 = 15k
	R15 = 33k
	R16 = 100k

Table 3.1. Resistor values for 8 and 16 switch beam position indicator

Latching relay control circuit

Some relays found on the surplus market have latching contacts. These are often found in test equipment where they are used to route signals that do not need to be switched very frequently. The current drawn when a large number of relays needs to be energised can be quite high and so the relays have a magnetic assistance to hold the contacts in one or the other position. To change the contacts over the relay coil is pulsed with a current for a short time, the relay armature moves and the magnet then holds the contacts closed in that position. To return the contacts the current in the relay coil is pulsed with the opposite polarity.

These relays are normally very high quality and are often designed for 24 to 30V. Some I obtained were made by Hewlett Packard (see photo opposite) and were stripped from a redundant switching matrix for testing microwave equipment. These relays are specified from DC to 18GHz with SMA connectors and have very low insertion loss and good VSWR performance.

The latching circuit is shown in **Fig 3.19.**

The circuit is controlled by the Tx input that is high when the transmitter is on. The voltage at the Tx input point is taken from a convenient switched supply rail in the transceiver. During receive TR1 is off and TR2 base is pulled up to the supply rail by R3, so turning TR2 hard on. This sends 24V to the relay coil and the current charges up C3 via the relay coil. The relay coil current flows from the 24V supply to C3. When C3 has charged up, the current flowing in the relay coil falls to zero. TR2 remains turned on hard during receive so replacing any charge lost in C3 due to internal leakage currents. When the Tx signal goes high TR1 turns on and TR2 turns off. TR3 is now turned fully on and the charge stored in C3 is discharged in the opposite polarity via the relay coil. The current now flows from C3 via the relay coil and is discharged to ground by TR3. The amplitude of the current pulses and the time for which the current pulses flow is dependent on the value of C3 and the coil resistance. Note that the value of C3 should not be

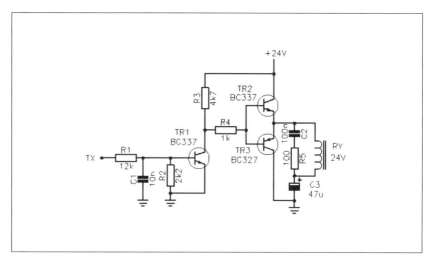

Fig 3.19. Latching relay drive circuit

too large; the value shown suited the HP relay with a coil resistance of 390Ω, increasing C3 to greater than 330µF caused the relay to miss pulses and it would get out of step with the control signal. C3 should be rated at 25V or greater. Most latching relays only require about a 10ms long pulse to cause the contacts to change over. Once the armature has passed the halfway point the magnet pulls the armature fully across to the other contact. Resistor R5 and C2 clamp the back EMF transients during the relay switching.

The speed at which the relay can be switched is mainly determined by the value of C3 and the mechanical inertia of

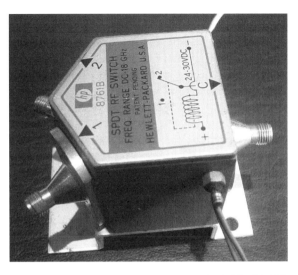

Fig 3.20. HP Microwave latching relay

the relay, so they may not be suitable for very rapid repetitive switching but should be OK for Tx / Rx switching. To reverse the contact arrangement means we need to swap over the leads to the relay coil to get the correct switching action. For the HP relay shown the coil needs to be pulsed with a positive polarity on the wire marked '+' with respect to the negative lead to make the contact for port 1 connect to the common port. To reverse the switching sense the positive is connected to the terminal marked '-'.

If the input is connected to the PTT rail in the transceiver the switching will be reversed, TR1 being on when on receive because the PTT rail is pulled high on receive and grounded during transmit. By reversing the relay wires the relay will assume the correct sense.

Alternative latching relay circuit

Some latching relays are designed for continuous coil energisation. These are normally 24V or higher voltage coils with a high resistance. Because the coil resistance is high the current can be allowed to flow continuously without any damage occurring to the relay coil. The limitation to pulsing the coil with opposite polarities is the inductance of the coil. For a high resistance coil the inductance will also be high, as much as 1 Henry in some cases. The time constant of L and R becomes a factor and limits the rate at which the relay can be switched repetitively between the two states.

For this type of relay an alternative driver is often used. This is known as the *'H-Bridge'* circuit because of its topology.

The input at the Rx / Tx control pin determines which polarity the relay is energised with. TR1 is turned on when Rx / Tx is high, pulling the collector voltage to ground and so TR2 and TR5 are turned off. TR6 is connected to the collector of TR1 via R8 and so will also be turned off. The voltage on the collector of TR6 will be high and hence TR3 and TR4 will be turned on. The current in the relay coil therefore flows from TR4 via the relay

47

Fig 3.21. H-Bridge switching circuit

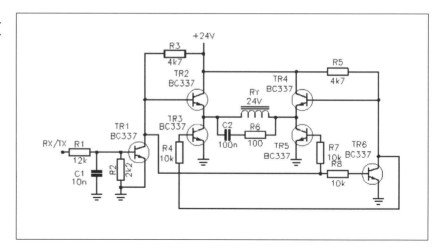

coil and is grounded by TR3 (see **Fig 3.21**).

When the Rx / Tx inputs goes low TR1 is turned off and the voltage at the collector will rise to the supply rail, so turning on TR2 and TR5 and via TR6 turning off TR3 and TR4. The current now flows via TR2 through the relay coil and to ground by TR5. Hence, the current now flows in the opposite direction.

C2 and R6 connected in series across the coil clamp the back EMF spikes generated when the coil polarity is reversed.

Variable duty cycle oscillator

Many applications require a continuously variable duty cycle. One application could be to vary the speed of a DC motor driving a rotator or elevator. This circuit also makes an excellent lamp dimmer for 12V lamps.

The circuit shown in **Fig 3.22** generates a rectangular pulse with a constant off time and the variable on time controlled by a linear pot. The

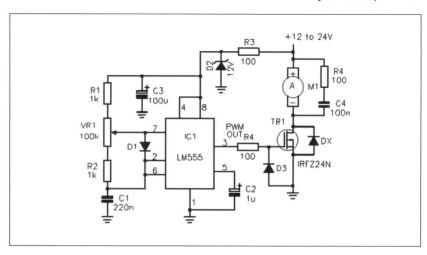

Fig 3.22. Variable duty cycle oscillator

48

output signal at pin 3 is a square wave of amplitude equal to the supply voltage; the duty cycle can be varied between about 2% and 98%. Using this circuit to drive a suitable power transistor feeding a DC motor can give a smooth and continuously variable speed control with maximum torque throughout the speed range.

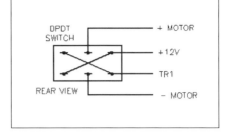

Fig 3.23. Pin view of typical double-pole change-over switch for reversing motor direction

The IC is the ubiquitous 555 timer with the variable on time set by the position of the VR1 slider. Diode D1 is a small signal type such as 1N914 or 1N4148. The frequency of the oscillator is determined by the value of C1 which is alternatively charged and discharged by the potential divider chain with D1 allowing different charge and discharge paths. With the values shown the off time is approx 1ms. When the slider of VR1 is turned so that it is connected to R1 the duty cycle is 98%. When the VR1 slider is connected to R2 the duty cycle is at the minimum value.

Transistor TR1 and DX should be selected to suit the peak current anticipated. A possible device is the BDX33C NPN Darlington, although a mosfet is shown in the schematic. DX clamps the back EMF spikes generated by the rapid switching of the inductive motor current. The BDX33C is a 10A / 100V device in a TO-220 package and will require heatsinking. It has a current gain of approx 1000. DX could be a 1N5402.

A mosfet such as an IRFZ-24N can handle a peak drain current of 49A. Note: if a mosfet is used DX is not required as all mosfets have this diode inherently built in. If a mosfet is used the supply voltage on IC1 must be greater than 8V and the maximum voltage on the mosfet gate is limited to 15V. A 12V zener can be used for D3 to clamp the gate drive if a supply voltage of more than 15V is used. The maximum safe supply voltage on the 555 timer IC is 15V.

A double-pole change-over switch can be used to reverse the rotation of the motor, as shown in **Fig 3.23**.

Liquid level monitor

In some applications it is necessary to switch a circuit on or off when the level of liquid is below or above a certain level. The circuit shown in **Fig 3.24** is the basis for a control system.

Water - although a reasonably good non-conductor of electricity - can be sensed by high impedance Op-Amplifiers with electrodes inserted into the liquid. The electrodes can be printed circuit board pattern of fingers with a ground track. An alternative is a PTFE feed-through insulator inserted through the metal wall of the liquid tank with a wire attached and the tank forming the ground electrode.

The Op-Amp used for IC1 needs to be a very high input resistance and the best choice is a JFET type such as the CA3240. This is a dual op-amp with an input resistance of about 1000MΩ. Alternatively the single version (CA3140) could be used, where only one input is required. Hence, it

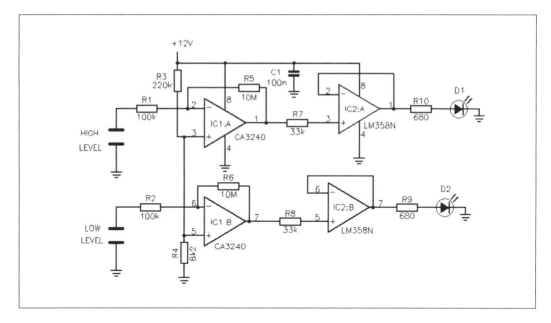

Fig 3.24. Liquid level detector

only requires a very small current to flow in the liquid to generate enough voltage to cause the amplifier to output a sizable voltage. Even de-ionised water has sufficient conductivity to pass a few µA. Fuels such as petrol or diesel, or engine oil, contain sufficient water to make it slightly conductive. This could be used as an indication of a high or low level condition.

Resistors R3 and R4 set a bias voltage of approx 0.5V. A leakage current of 1µA flowing to ground at either input will cause the op-amp output to switch high by approx 10V. This is buffered by a second op-amp, which can be a normal type such as a 741 or the dual LM358N, and this then turns on an LED. The outputs of IC2 could be used to turn a pump on and off to maintain a constant level in the liquid tank.

CHAPTER 4

Power supply circuits

In this chapter:

- 12V to 24V boost converter
- A simple high current regulator
- 1.5A variable voltage bench power supply
- Solar panel battery charger
- High stability screen grid stabiliser
- Nickel Cadmium battery charger
- Adjustable zener
- Fast electronic fuse
- High power zener
- Nickel Cadmium cell 'zapper'
- Nickel Cadmium cell rejuvenator
- Negative voltage generator
- Stabilised supply noise filter
- Simple reverse polarity protection
- Low voltage step-down converter
- Simple add on screen grid stabiliser

 OR THOSE applications where a simple step-up DC converter is required the 'Boost Converter' is a good choice when the output current required isn't too high.

12V to 24V boost converter

A boost converter can deliver an efficiency of around 90%. The output is not inherently short circuit proof because of the topology and so adequate fusing should be fitted to the input. The circuit shown is dimensioned to provide a maximum of 1A of output current.

A basic boost converter is shown in **Fig 4.1** using the UC3843B and a low cost mosfet. The UC3843B is an 8-pin DIL IC containing everything except the power switch. The mosfet chosen is the International Rectifier IRFZ-24N that has a suitably low on-resistance and can safely handle up to 17A of rms current and 68A of peak current. At 24W power output it requires

Fig 4.1. 12V to
24V boost con-
verter

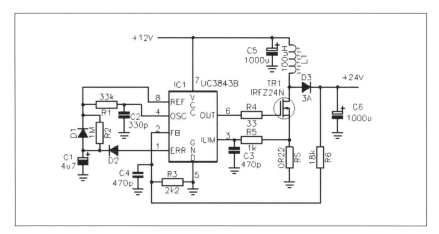

little heatsinking. The circuit will operate from approx 9V to 16V and provide an efficiency of about 90% at 1A output current.

The UC3843B features an under-voltage lockout threshold of 8.4V so if the input supply voltage falls to less than this level the circuit will be shut down and restart when the supply voltage rises above the threshold. In automotive applications this provides protection should the battery voltage fall below 8.4V whilst the engine is being cranked. Another device in the series is the UC3842B but this has an under-voltage lockout threshold of about 16V so it is unsuitable for 12V automotive applications.

The boost converter operates in a 'flyback' mode by alternatively storing energy in the form of magnetic flux in an inductor when the mosfet is turned on and then releasing it to the output when the mosfet is turned off. Because the switching frequency is high the value of inductor required is quite small and occupies very little volume. The inductor is wound on a powdered iron core made by Micrometals and able to supply up to 1A of output current. The core material is type 26 and the core diameter is 1.06in (27mm). The part number is T106-26 and is colour coded white / yellow. The storage inductor is wound with 22SWG enameled copper wire with 33 turns. The boost converter operates at about 100kHz, which is set by R1 and C2 on the oscillator input (pin 4).

The feedback resistors R3 and R6 set the output voltage. The internal reference voltage is 2.5V. The converter features a soft start circuit to reduce the inrush current at switch on. The components D1, C1, D2 and R2 form the soft start circuit. D1 and D2 are 1N4148 or 1N914 types. C1 should be a low leakage tantalum capacitor. The inductor peak current, and hence the maximum power output, is set by the low value resistor Rs in the source of TR1. The voltage developed across Rs is a replica of the triangular waveform drain current and is filtered by R5 and C3 and fed to the current limit input of IC1. Rs needs to be a high wattage resistor and a 2W wire-wound would be the best choice for this component. The gate drive to TR1 is via R4 to suppress ringing caused by the Miller effect in the mosfet.

The output rectifier diode D3 should be a Schottky for the best efficiency and a type rated at 3A average current is the optimum choice with a

PIV rating of at least 30V. A suitable device would be the International Rectifier 31DQ03. Ultra-fast diodes will also work with a slightly lower efficiency. A suitable device would be a BYV28-50 or MUR310. Normal silicon rectifier diodes such as 1N4000 or 1N5400 series are far too slow to work effectively at 100kHz and should not be used.

The output smoothing capacitor C6 needs to be a type designed for switch-mode supply applications and having a low ESR to reduce the output ripple voltage and able to sustain high peak ripple current. An ESR of less than 0.25Ω is needed if the output ripple voltage is to be less than 100mV p-p. The peak charging current into C6 is approximately the same as the average input current and so a diode and smoothing capacitor capable of handling high peak current is required. A suitable type would be a Nichicon PJ series rated at 35V and having a value of at least $1000\mu F$. The input capacitor C5 can also be a Nichicon PJ type or a normal electrolytic because the ripple current it experiences is not as severe as C6.

All the resistors except Rs can be 1/4W or 1/2W types. TR1 will require a small heatsink with an insulating washer and mounting bush to prevent the drain shorting to ground. Because of the high circulating currents the grounding of components around IC1 and the mosfet is critical. Although the frequency is only 100kHz the construction should use short leads and low inductance grounding similar to VHF construction techniques.

One or two points about boost converters need to be appreciated. The first is that the power to be converted has to come from the input supply. For a converter with an input voltage range of 9 to 16V the input current will be highest when the input voltage is 9V. With an efficiency of 90% the input power required is 1.1 x 24 = 26.4W and with a 9V supply this is an average current of 3A. When the input voltage is 16V the average input current is about 1.7A. If the input supply cannot deliver the required current the converter will not operate correctly. Many linear regulated power supplies, although capable of supplying the average current, are not able to supply the high input current pulses that a boost converter draws. Although the average input current is only 3A the peak current can be several times this figure for a short period when the mosfet turns on. If the linear supply runs into current limit the converter will 'hiccup' and behave erratically. When testing a boost converter using a linear regulated bench supply as the input

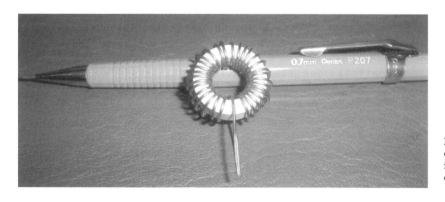

Fig 4.2. Boost converter inductor wound on T106-26 core

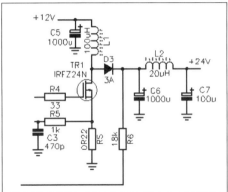

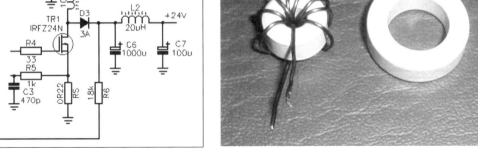

Fig 4.3. Additional output filter

Fig 4.4. Output filter inductor (left) and T106-26 core (right)

source it is often necessary to connect a large electrolytic capacitor (10,000µF or more) across the bench supply output to help supply the pulsing peak current.

If the output ripple voltage needs to be less than 100mV then rather than increasing the value of C6 it is better to insert an additional filter LC network in series with the output. This can be a small inductor also wound on 26 material (T50-26) and having a value of about 10 to 20% of the main switching inductor. This with an electrolytic capacitor of about 100µF will reduce the ripple voltage to about 10mV.

For applications requiring more output current the value of Rs can be reduced. If Rs is set to 0.1Ω the converter can supply up to 2A. The rectifier diode will need to be a 5A device and the value of C6 will need to be larger; a value of 2 x 1000µF PJ types in parallel will suffice.

A simple high current regulator

Many items of amateur equipment do not require very critical voltage control. Where an item such as this needs a high current supply we can save some money by using a circuit called the 'bucket regulator'. This regulator is capable of supplying high current with a voltage regulation of about 1% accuracy. A typical application would be a battery charger for a lead-acid battery supplying the shack 12V equipment.

The regulator requires a high current secondary and a bridge rectifier. For a battery charger the best option is a transformer designed for this application with a flux limited core. Often a suitable transformer can be salvaged from an old battery charger.

The circuit is detailed in **Fig 4.5** and it uses a thyristor (SCR) to control the current into the battery.

The supply uses a high current secondary and a bridge rectifier to provide an unsmoothed DC to the SCR. The transformer secondary voltage should be approximately the output voltage divided by 1.2, hence for a 12V lead-acid battery, which when fully charged is 14V, the secondary voltage

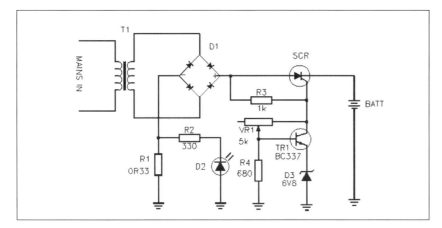

Fig 4.5. Bucket regulator circuit

needs to be at least 11V. A good choice would be a transformer with two 6.3V / 5A heater windings connected in series.

The bucket regulator works like this. When the positive ripple voltage exceeds the threshold on the gate the SCR conducts and supplies charging current to the battery. The threshold is set by the adjustable zener comprising TR1 and associated components. The values shown suit a 12V battery and can be set to 14V by the preset VR1. When the battery voltage rises and equals the threshold voltage the SCR stops conducting. It is the periodic topping up of the battery that gives the bucket regulator its name.

Each time the SCR conducts, the LED D2 flashes because it is connected in the return leg of the bridge and the current flowing in R1 causes a voltage drop. With the component values shown the maximum charging current is about 6A. The transformer, bridge rectifier and SCR need to be adequately rated for the anticipated current. The return resistor R1 also needs to be sized accordingly, higher currents require a lower value for R1. In the circuit R1 is 0.33Ω and consists of 3 x 1Ω 5W wire-wound resistors connected in parallel.

When the battery is fully charged the regulator stops switching until the voltage falls by a small amount, perhaps due to a small current being drawn. The SCR will turn on for successive half cycles until the battery voltage again rises to the threshold voltage. For a zero current load condition the LED will flash every few seconds because of the inherent internal discharge of the lead-acid battery and the lost energy will be replenished. The charger can be permanently connected with no danger of damage to the lead-acid battery because of the close voltage control.

Replacing the battery with a large electrolytic capacitor converts the circuit into a high current supply suitable for powering audio amplifiers or an HF transceiver, provided the transformer can supply enough current. The voltage stability between zero and full load isn't spectacular but probably adequate for the average transceiver designed for 12V operation.

To set up the regulator connect a low value resistor across the output to draw about 25% of the rated current. Connect a capacitor of approx 1000µF in parallel with the load resistor. Adjust the preset VR1 to obtain the required cut out voltage.

1.5A variable voltage bench power supply

For many applications we require a simple bench power supply that can be varied in output voltage and able to supply 1A or so to power a circuit being developed. The circuit shown in **Fig 4.6** is a simple power supply using the LM-317 integrated circuit.

The heart of the bench supply is IC1, the National Semiconductors LM-317 in the popular TO-220 package. This IC can deliver an output voltage of 1.2V to over 30V when fed from a suitable transformer, bridge rectifier and smoothing capacitor. In this bench supply the output voltage can be varied between about 2V to 15V and the output voltage and current are displayed using a 1mA moving coil meter.

The supply requires a transformer with a secondary voltage of 15V AC and a current rating of 2A. The secondary voltage is rectified by the bridge rectifier consisting of D1 to D4 and smoothed by C1 and C2, which are 25V rating.

TR1 and the associated components perform the current limiting with R1 being the current sensing element in series with the output. R1 should be a 2W wire-wound resistor. The current limit is selectable between two limits, either 300mA or 1.5A by SW2. R4, R5 and R6 are also 2W wire-wound resistors. The voltage is set by VR1. The supply has a floating output and either the positive or negative output terminal can be used as the common, enabling the supply to provide a negative voltage if required. The meter displays either voltage or current by moving SW1 to the required position. The voltage full scale of 15V is set by the calibration preset VR3. VR2 sets the current range to 1.5A.

IC1 requires a heatsink and the device tab needs to be isolated from ground by an insulating washer and mounting bush.

Fig 4.6. 1.5A bench supply

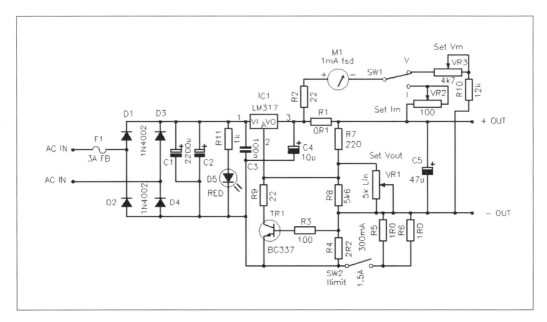

Solar panel battery charger

A solar panel makes an excellent standby source of 12V power [at least in sunny South Africa! - Ed]. With a charge regulator and a lead-acid battery this is free power. Although the efficiency of solar panels is very low, around 3% at best, the sun provides plenty of irradiation to provide power. An average solar panel delivers about 40W of power with an output voltage of up to 18V when fully illuminated. The maximum output current is approx 2A.

The average solar panel requires a shunt regulator to operate correctly. The circuit shown in **Fig 4.7** suits a 40W panel and is self powered from the solar panel.

The solar panel SP1 is connected in parallel with the charging circuit and when the panel delivers sufficient energy the charger will deliver current to the lead-acid battery. The regulator uses an LM741 configured as a fixed voltage regulator operating as a constant voltage current sink. When the battery is fully charged the excess energy is dissipated in the shunt regulator transistor TR1. Hence, this device needs to be capable of dissipating up to 40W continuously and mounted on a good heatsink. The transistor chosen for TR1 is the TIP140 which is a Darlington offering high current gain.

The reference voltage for the regulator is provided by a 5.1V zener connected across the inverting input of IC1. The output voltage is set by VR1. D2 is a low volt drop rectifier; a Schottky would be the best choice although a normal silicon diode such as a 1N5402 will also work. D2 prevents the battery discharging into the regulator during periods of low solar illumination.

The best option is to mount the solar panel high up and with an unobstructed view of the sun. The two wires connect the solar panel to the charging circuit mounted close to the battery. A suitable fuse should be used in series with the battery and the equipment being powered to protect against accidental short circuits.

To set up the charging voltage a high power resistor of about 22Ω is

Fig 4.7. Solar panel battery charger

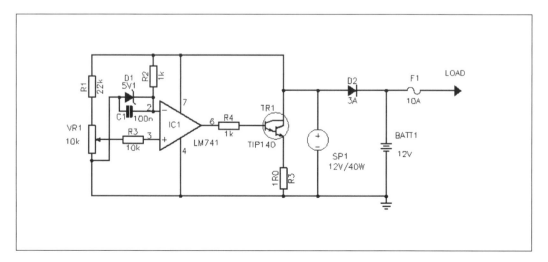

substituted for the battery and VR1 adjusted to the required fully charged voltage with the panel fully illuminated. Most 12V lead-acid batteries exhibit a terminal voltage of 14 to 14.5V when fully charged.

High stability screen grid stabiliser

Many tetrode valves for VHF / UHF linear amplifiers require a very stable screen grid supply that can sink and source current. A popular valve is the 4CX250 requiring a voltage of between 300 to 350V at a maximum current of 30mA. Because most of the 4CX250 valves exhibit negative screen current at low drive levels we cannot use a conventional series regulator. For this application the best option is a type of shunt regulator.

The shunt regulator is controlled by an op-amp in a negative feedback configuration. Because the voltage gain is high we need to use a low noise op-amp for IC1. A normal op-amp such as an LM741 is simply too noisy for the circuit to work the way it should. We have selected the NE5534N that is the same pinout as the LM741 but offers a much lower noise performance. It also requires less current to operate. For the same reason the reference voltage derived by D1 needs very good decoupling to eliminate the zener high frequency noise. If the zener is noisy it will effectively amplitude modulate the output voltage. The voltage gain in the circuit is about 60, being the 300V output divided by the 5.1V reference voltage. The supply voltage for the op-amp is derived from the unstabilised rail with a high value dropping resistor (R2) and a 12V / 1W zener diode (D2). The supply is powered from the unstabilised rail, which needs to be at least 400V.

The shunt regulator uses an International Rectifier IRF840 mosfet that is rated at 500V and 8A maximum drain current. The on-resistance of the IRF840 is approx 0.85Ω when fully saturated. However, in this applica-

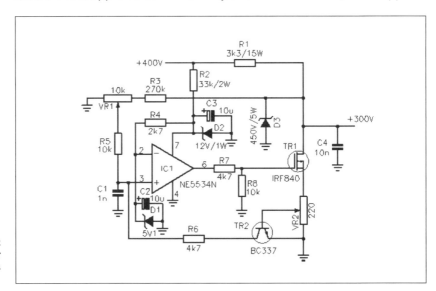

Fig 4.8. Shunt stabiliser for tetrode screen grid

tion the mosfet should never be turned fully on and it will act like a variable resistor with a fairly high resistance between drain and source. The maximum safe dissipation when correctly heatsinked is approx 50W.

The mosfet pulls current via R1 to bring the screen voltage to the required value. The mosfet is controlled with a positive voltage between gate and source and as the gate voltage increases the mosfet will turn on harder pulling the drain voltage towards ground. The gate threshold voltage is approx 2 to 4V to begin conducting. Because of the voltage divider (R7 and R8) between the op-amp output and the mosfet gate the op-amp output needs to be approx 6V before the mosfet starts to turn on. The reason this is used is because an op-amp is most linear over the range of voltage at around half its supply voltage, which here is 12V. The mosfet must be bolted to a good heatsink because it is dissipating a fair amount of power. At 300V drain-source voltage with 30mA flowing to ground the dissipation is 9W. When the tetrode screen grid is pushing current from the valve back to the shunt stabiliser the current flowing to ground in the mosfet is somewhat higher.

The output voltage stability of this supply is excellent, typically less than 20mV variation between zero current and the maximum of about 40mA (approx 0.006% variation). The output noise performance is also outstanding, being less than 1mV p-p ripple on the 300V output. However, this will only be achieved if the construction is satisfactory and the circuit is well screened from external noise sources such as high power RF from the amplifier.

R1 needs to have adequate power dissipation; the exact value will largely depend on the unstabilised supply voltage. R1 can be made up of several lower wattage resistors connected in series, 3 x 1kΩ resistors each rated at 5W will be about right for a single 4CX250 and a supply rail of about 400 to 450V. For a two-valve amplifier R1 will need to be lower in value, the exact value will again depend on the unstabilised supply voltage and the peak current required.

The maximum current able to be supplied to the screen grid is determined by the value of R1 and the unstabilised supply voltage, and how much it dips as the current drawn rises. If the supply is 400V and R1 is 3k3Ω the maximum current that can be drawn before the output voltage starts to fall out of regulation is about 40mA. When the screen grid is not demanding any screen current, such as when the amplifier is in standby mode, all the current flows to ground via TR1.

The source current of TR1 is monitored by VR2. The slider of VR2 is connected to the base of TR2 and if the voltage across the base-emitter junction exceeds approx 0.6V TR2 will start to turn on. The collector of TR2 is connected via R6 to the feedback input of IC1. When TR2 turns on the voltage will be pulled towards ground. This will cause IC1 to decrease the output voltage and start to turn off the mosfet, so pulling the drain voltage higher. This feature is necessary because some low emission 4CX250 valves have excessive negative screen current when the RF drive is zero or very low. Valves that have been subjected to excessive anode temperatures (i.e. valves that have been grossly over driven!) can exhibit negative screen current of 30mA or more. To set, first turn VR2 so no voltage appears at the base of TR2. With no load the preset VR1 is then adjusted to obtain the required screen grid voltage. Adjust VR2 so that the mosfet drain voltage just starts to decrease and then set VR2 so the voltage returns to normal. Any further increase in drain current will then cause the regulator to drop out of regulation.

The circuit shown in Fig 4.8 is dimensioned for a single 4CX250 drawing a maximum of 30mA screen grid current. If a design for a two-valve amplifier is required we need to increase the current to about 60mA by changing the current limit resistor. The simplest method is to shunt VR2 with a 220Ω resistor.

To turn the screen grid off during receive all we need to do is to switch the 300V supply with a relay contact controlled by the amplifier PTT line. This relay should be a changeover type with the common contact connected to the screen grid. The make contact is then connected to the 300V output and the break contact is connected to ground. Hence, when in receive mode the 300V is disconnected and the screen grid is grounded to prevent shot noise.

If the unstabilised supply is greater than 500V, a zener of about 450V and 5W dissipation must be connected between the drain of TR1 and ground to limit the off load voltage to below the 500V rating of the mosfet.

Nickel Cadmium battery charger

Many items of equipment use rechargeable batteries, from handheld radios to items found around the home such as cordless drills and other tools. Often the battery charger supplied with these items is of very poor quality and may lead to reduced battery life because of over charging. As rechargeable batteries are quite expensive to buy it makes sense to use the best charger available to maximise the life.

The circuit detailed in **Fig 4.9** and **Fig 4.10** is a 'deluxe' charger that not only limits the charging current to the correct value but also incorporates a timer to switch off the charger after the nominal charging time has expired. This prevents damage if a cell in the battery pack has developed a reverse polarity mode, which is caused by deep discharge or a long period of inactivity.

The charger can handle batteries from the popular AA cell up to D size cells of 4AH. By selecting the component values the charger can be customised to suit the battery pack to be charged. With sufficient ingenuity it would be possible to make a 'universal charger' by switching various components into circuit to suit the battery type.

Fig 4.9. Current limited battery charger

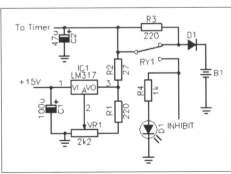

The manufacturers normal recommended charging current for normal Ni-Cd and Ni-Mh cells is between C/10 and C/5 depending on the cell type, where C is the capacity in Ampere-Hours (AH). Fast charge cells normally use C/5 and other types use C/10. A normal charge level AA cell is nominally 500mAH and so will require a constant current charge of 50mA. A D size cell is nominally 4AH and so the correct constant current charging rate is 400mA. The time to recharge a standard charge level battery is normally 14 hours at C/10 assuming the battery is discharged to the 1V/cell level.

The constant current charger uses an LM-317 voltage regulator. This device can be set to 1.2V to over 30V with just two resistors and is capable of supplying up to 1.5A current. The output current is limited to the required value by a low value resistor (R2) in series with the output. The charging circuit is shown in Fig 4.9. When the charger is first switched on, the current drawn by the battery pack is limited due to the series resistor. The LM-317 delivers a constant voltage and as the battery charges the voltage appearing across the battery rises towards the fully charged condition. The recommended fully charged voltage of a Ni-Cd cell is approx 1.45V / cell.

In many cases the battery may not be totally discharged and we have no easy way of telling the amount of charge remaining in the cells. There is no harm in charging a partially discharged cell. People who do not understand how the cell chemistry works have written a lot of rubbish over the years. A cell has a finite number of charge / discharge cycles before it no longer attains its full capacity. Most manufacturers put a capacity limit of 80% of the nominal on the end of useful life parameter.

A typical Ni-Cd cell can sustain about 2000 charge and discharge cycles down to 1V / cell before the capacity falls to 80%. However, if you only discharge the cell to 50% of its rated capacity and then recharge it you will achieve about twice the normal charge / discharge cycles before the cell falls to the 80% capacity level.

It is the chemical usage that causes this. There is only so much electrolyte contained in the cell and when it is partially depleted the capacity starts to fall off. Extrapolating the capacity curve against charge / discharge cycles shows that for a 25% discharge and then recharging gives about four times the normal number of cycles.

The LM-317 is adjusted by VR1 to the required output voltage. The input voltage to the LM-317 needs to be at least 3V greater than the output voltage. The exact cut out voltage will depend on the cell type and manufacturer. The number of cells in the battery will determine this. Different manufacturers have different recommended cut out voltages depending on the application. The spread is typically between about 1.4V / cell up to as high as 1.55V / cell. For example, a nominal 9V battery for a handheld radio consists of seven cells and the nominal voltage is 8.4V, but the fully charged voltage will be approx 7 x 1.45V = 10.15V. It would be advisable to check with the manufacturer what the safe maximum voltage is before adjusting the cut out voltage.

When the battery is first connected the relay contact is closed shorting out R3, and the charging current causing a voltage drop across R2 will hold down the voltage. As the battery reaches the fully charged condition the terminal voltage will rise to the 1.45V / cell condition. When this occurs the voltage difference across R2 will fall to almost zero and only a very small trickle charge current will flow into the battery. Provided the cut off voltage is correctly set by VR1 the battery can be left connected indefinitely. The value of R2 determines the maximum charging current and should be selected accordingly.

D1 prevents the battery discharging back into the circuit should the

This charging method is not the usual constant current mode normally used for Ni-Cd cells. In a true constant current charger the current when fully charged is the same as the initial charging current when the battery is discharged. The problem with constant current charging is that the cell terminal voltages can reach unsafe levels and consequent liberation of gas that can lead to premature failure. If the internal gas pressure rises too high the safety vent opens and electrolyte is lost. If this is performed on a regular basis the cell will have a very short life.

Some of the techniques used in the past are to monitor the cell temperature and to terminate the charge when the cell exceeds a certain temperature, hopefully before the gassing point. This is only successful for a limited type of Ni-Cd cell. The best method would be to monitor the internal gas pressure and terminate the charge when it starts to rise because of gassing. Some large industrial Ni-Cd cells have this feature but the smaller cells cannot be fitted with the pressure pipe and sensor required.

Another method is to try to measure the very small change in the cell voltage when the gassing begins. Typically we need to be able to measure about a 2mV difference in the cell voltage as it begins to gas. This can work with some Ni-Cd cells but isn't always accurate enough. Hence, the safer option is the method used in this charger and this is known in the industry as 'taper charging', as it is a mixture of constant current and constant voltage. Of all the charging methods it is the only one that is 100% safe, although the charging time can be longer than other types.

input supply fail. As this has a bearing on the available terminal voltage it would be optimum to use a low voltage drop diode such as a 1N5819 Schottky. However, because we can compensate for the additional voltage drop with VR1 a normal silicon diode is adequate. For most applications a 1N4002 will suffice. The LM-317 will require bolting to a suitable heatsink with an insulating washer between the tab and any grounded metalwork.

The control of RY1 is by the timer circuit in **Fig 4.10**. When 14 hours has elapsed the relay RY1 will be energised so inserting the additional resistor R3 in series to limit the trickle charge current. This is a useful safety feature because the cell may not have reached its fully charged voltage because of an internal partial short. Irrespective of whether the cell has reached the fully charged voltage or not the charger will enter the trickle charge routine after 14 hours.

The value of R3 should be about nine times the value of R2.

To set up the charger, connect a resistor across the output in place of the battery. The resistor needs to be a fairly high value to simulate the fully charged condition. In most cases a 4k7Ω will suffice. Adjust VR1 to obtain the correct cut off voltage.

The timer circuit uses a binary divider and logic gate square wave oscillator. The IC is the On-Semi (previously Motorola Semiconductors)

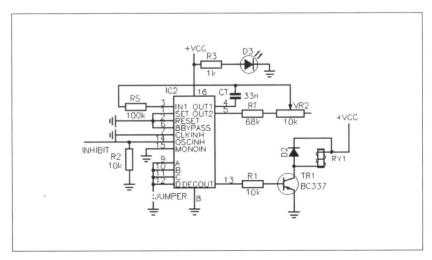

Fig 4.10. 14-hour timer circuit for battery charger

In many battery packs one or more cells may flip polarity during discharge because they have a lower capacity than the other cells. If the cell stays in the reverse polarity condition, which is normally the case, the fully charged voltage may be one or more cell voltage below the correct value. The danger is that these flipped polarity cells are now being charged in the wrong polarity and will gas violently and probably expire.

When a battery pack is assembled the manufacturers normally use well-matched cells so the difference in the individuals cells capacity is as small as possible. Cheap battery packs rarely meet these criteria. However, although when first assembled the cells may be within a few percent of each other, the capacity throughout the life of the battery pack will vary and the originally well-matched cells will drift away and eventually one or more cells will be mismatched and lower in capacity.

The only guaranteed way to flip the cell back to the correct polarity is to isolate it from the others and then 'zap' it with a large electrolytic capacitor charged up to about 30V. This will often salvage an otherwise junk battery pack. After several charge and discharge cycles the pack should return to full capacity. The danger of constant current charging is that it doesn't know a cell or two may have flipped polarity and then severe damage may occur to the whole battery pack.

MC14536B CMOS logic circuit. The same device is made by a number of manufacturers; ST-Microelectronics part number is the HCC/HCF4536B. The IC is in a 16-pin DIL package and operates over the supply voltage range of 3 to 15V. This IC contains a 2^{24} binary counter and latch as well as the oscillator. The oscillator requires two resistors and a capacitor to set the frequency (RT, RS and CT). The fine setting of the frequency is by VR2, which allows RT to be varied. The capacitor used for CT needs to have good temperature stability and a polyester foil capacitor is the optimum type if the best accuracy is required. If the time isn't that critical within a half-hour or so then a ceramic capacitor may be used.

When the IC is powered up the oscillator runs and the binary divider counts down to zero. When the count reaches zero the output latch is set and this can be used to control an external circuit. The total binary count is 16.7772 million clock pulses.

The required oscillator frequency is 16.7772 million divided by the number of seconds in 14 hours. 14 hours is 14 x 3600 seconds or 50,400 seconds. Hence, the clock period required is 3ms. The counter decrements on every rising edge of the clock waveform. As there are two pulses for each clock cycle in a binary divider, this is a frequency of 166.66Hz. The last 16 stages of the counter can be configured to change the divider ratio with four control lines in a BCD format. This allows different divider counts to be selected. The four control pins are left floating to select the maximum count.

The binary counter is split into three sections each of 2^8 or 256 counts, so the total count is 256 x 256 x 256. In order to speed up the testing the sections can be bypassed so a simulated 14-hour timer can be tested in a few seconds with the correct oscillator frequency. This is performed by the jumper link between the BCD control pins. For normal operation the BCD pins are floating or ungrounded and the internal pull-up resistors set the inputs high. When BCD pins are grounded the binary counter has only eight stages enabled and hence the counter will clock over in 2^8 clock pulses. This is a total divider ratio of 256 clock pulses and hence with the required oscillator frequency will latch the relay after 1.53 seconds.

When the counter has reached zero the output at pin 13 goes high and turns on the transistor TR1 controlling RY1. A second contact on RY1 supplies a high logic level to pin 14 of the MC14536B that stops the counter advancing any further. Without this clock inhibit signal the counter would roll over after another 14 hours and start the charger again. The charger will remain in the trickle charge mode indefinitely until the charger is switched off. Hence, it can be switched on and left for extended periods with no danger to the battery pack being charged.

This charger may also be used for charging small lead-acid gel-cells with an appropriate regulator IC and current limiting resistor. A 12V / 7AH gel-cell should be charged at a maximum current of 700mA and a cut off voltage of 14.0V.

Adjustable zener

Very often we need a particular value zener for a project but find the ones in the junk box are the wrong value. This simple circuit demonstrates the use of a zener with a transistor to make a variable voltage current sink. The circuit acts like an amplified zener but with a somewhat higher current rating than a normal zener.

Fig 4.11. Adjustable zener

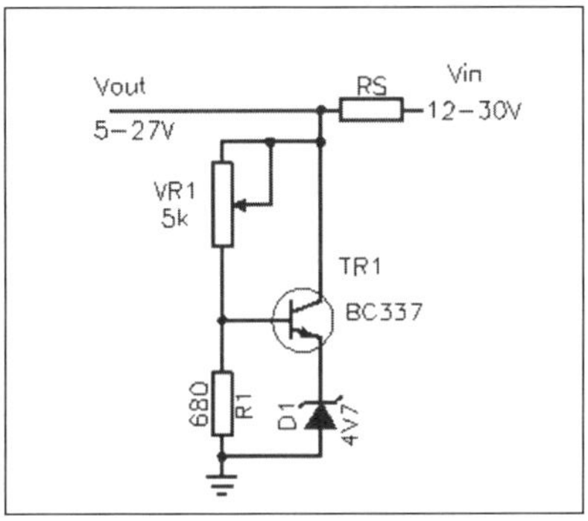

The lowest resulting output voltage is slightly higher than the value of the zener so this needs to be considered when selecting a suitable zener. The current sink capabilities are also dependent on the zener power rating. If a 500mW type is used the maximum current will be about 100mA. For high voltage applications the transistor used needs to have adequate dissipation and a heatsink may be required. The supply voltage and output current required determine the value of RS.

Fast electronic fuse

In many items of equipment fusing is a necessity to protect the item from damage due to a short circuit. When a fuse blows the possibility is that a replacement is not immediately available. This circuit uses four transistors to simulate a very fast fuse to interrupt the current if the current exceeds a limit. The circuit is reset with a push button.

TR2 is a power transistor capable of passing the required maximum current and suitably heatsinked. TR1 is a medium power transistor to drive TR2. The current level required will determine suitable components for TR1 and TR2. (TR1 and TR2 could be combined into a common Darlington package). TR3 and TR4 are connected as a thyristor (SCR) and when the return current flowing in RS develops a voltage of about 0.6V TR4 will begin to turn on. When the collector voltage of TR4 starts to fall it turns on TR3 which supplies extra base current to TR4 hence it will turn on more. Because of the configuration this causes the combination of TR3 and TR4 to be regenerative and the pair will quickly latch hard on, so pulling the base of TR1 to ground. This switches off TR1 and TR2 so protecting the equipment. The circuit will remain latched until the reset button SW1 is pressed. This allows the circuit to resume normal operation. Should the fault condition still exist the circuit will latch off again. If the short has been removed the circuit operates normally.

There will be a small voltage drop across TR2 and this should be allowed for when the supply feeding the fuse is set up. This circuit can be added to an existing power supply and the voltage sensing feedback resistor for the power supply taken from the point V_{out}, hence including the fuse within the feedback loop.

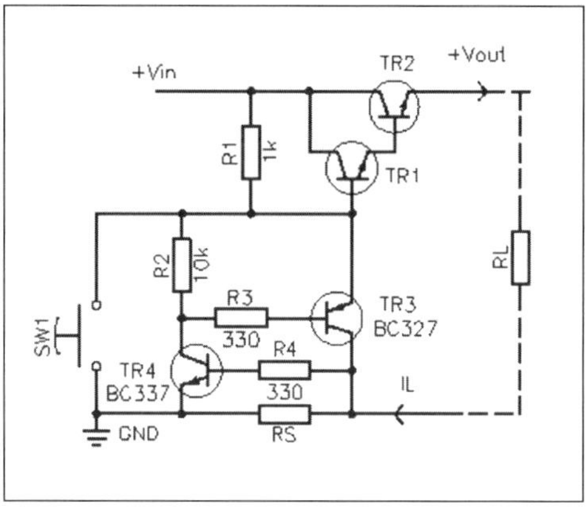

Fig 4.12. Resettable electronic fuse

High power zener

Many circuits require a high power zener but often a suitable type is either unobtainable or simply too expensive. The circuit in **Fig 4.13** uses a low power zener diode and a PNP power transistor to simulate a high power zener.

The transistor used for TR1 should have adequate voltage and power rating. The configuration is convenient because the collector of TR1 can be bolted directly to ground without an insulating washer, so improving the heatsinking. Using a 1W zener for D1 and a transistor rated at 4A or more the circuit simulates a zener with 80W dissipation. Resistor RL needs to be appropriately chosen.

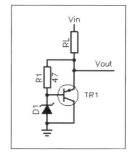

Fig 4.13. High power zener

Nickel Cadmium cell 'zapper'

Nickel Cadmium cells can develop a partial internal short due to long periods of inactivity. All Ni-Cd cells suffer from this, especially those that are not used very often, such as cordless screwdrivers and other items of domestic appliances. The cell may appear to take a normal charge and the terminal voltage immediately after charging is often correct but the cell quickly loses its charge over a few days or even hours.

This is caused by what is known as a 'soft-short' across the cell. This is the result of a crystalline growth between the two plates of the cell and is often a few hundred ohms to as much as a few kilohms. If not removed this will cause the cell gradually to grow worse as the short becomes harder (lower resistance) because the chemical growth increases.

What most amateurs do not realise is that all Ni-Cd cells will self-discharge, due to the inherent internal leakage current, down to zero cell voltage in a period of about three months, irrespective of the charge-state when placed in storage. Elevated ambient temperatures will accelerate the

A military base here in South Africa is located in an area where ambient temperatures of +35°C or more are common in the summer. The warehouse is not air-conditioned. The roof is made of corrugated iron and the internal temperature on a summer day was often in excess of +60°C. The warehouse is used to store man-pack radios and battery packs. The annual loss of revenue due to battery packs deteriorating was high. The supplier of the battery packs was very happy with the situation because the annual sales of replacement battery packs amounted to millions of rand. By purchasing a number of ex-supermarket freezers at a nominal cost to store the battery packs the annual costs dropped dramatically, so saving a large drain on the taxpayers money!

discharge; storing Ni-Cd battery packs in the freezer will slow down the self-discharge rate. Hence, there is no real benefit to be gained by charging the cell before placing it in storage, it will simply take a little longer to discharge to zero volts.

A common way of removing a soft short is to charge a large electrolytic capacitor up to about 30V and then discharge the capacitor into the cell. The very large current spike blows the soft short similar to a fuse. This is commonly known as 'zapping' the cell. A large constant charging current does not normally remove a soft short and so this technique is not as effective and can cause excessive gassing in the cell. Zapping a cell with a high voltage and high current pulse is a safe way to remove the internal shorts. The affected cell *must* be isolated from the rest of the battery pack for this to be successful. Most battery packs can be carefully split open and the individual cells terminals accessed. Measure each cell voltage in turn and determine which cell(s) are very low in terminal voltage and mark them in some way. (Some cells may reverse polarity under heavy discharge and these must be returned to the correct polarity before charging. Zapping is a quick and safe way to achieve this).

A quick and easy way to tell if the cells in the battery pack are working correctly, is to charge each cell via a low value resistor connected in series with a 12V 1A supply for a short time (seconds rather than minutes!) A resistor of about 330Ω / 5W normally works. Connect a voltmeter across the cell and watch the cell terminal voltage as the 12V supply is switched on. If the cell voltage rises quickly to around 1.2V the cell is probably OK. Time the charging current to be, say, 30s for each cell. Perform this test on each cell and then leave the battery pack for 24 hours. After 24 hours any cell with a problem will be much lower in voltage than good cells.

For those amateurs who do not have a bench power supply able to give 30V a good alternative is to use a boost converter from 12V to charge up a zapping capacitor. A circuit I made some time ago is shown in **Fig 4.14**.

This uses a 10W audio amplifier IC as a square wave generator that doubles the input voltage and charges up a large electrolytic capacitor. The IC chosen behaves like an LM741 with a 3.5A output stage. (In fact this circuit was one I designed for a 10W hand-held VHF transceiver that had a Ni-Cd battery pack with 11 cells, which when fully charged was about 15.6V. This meant it couldn't be charged from a normal 12V vehicle because the 12V battery in the vehicle only rose to 14.4V when the alternator was charging, and with the engine off the battery voltage sank to around 13V. Hence, the need to generate a higher voltage to feed the charge regulator).

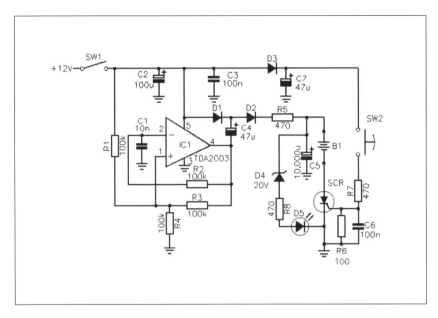

Fig 4.14. Ni-Cd cell 'zapper'

The cell to be zapped (B1) is connected between the charged capacitor C5 and a high current SCR. The voltage doubler uses IC1, a TDA-2003 audio amplifier IC, to generate ≈12V square wave pulses. R2 and C1 set the frequency of oscillation of about 1kHz. The output of IC1 is coupled via C4 to the voltage doubler diodes D1 and D2. These diodes can be 1N4002 because the frequency is quite low and efficiency isn't an issue for this circuit. The peak voltage appearing at R5 is approx 24V. This charges up C5 slowly because of the value of R5. When C5 has fully charged the LED will be lit as the zener turns on at 20V. The oscillator is now switched off by opening SW1. When push button SW2 is pressed the SCR gate is driven positive by the charge stored in C7 and the SCR turns on discharging the capacitor via the cell being zapped.

SCR needs to be a high current thyristor such as a BT-152 or larger. A relay contact or push button switch could be substituted for the SCR but the contacts will be eroded rapidly because of the high inrush current.

To use, connect the cell to be zapped by a pair of leads with crocodile clips, ensuring the polarity is correct. Connect a voltmeter across the cell to indicate the terminal voltage. Switch on SW1 and wait for the large capacitor to charge up, which will take a few seconds. Switch off SW1 and press SW2 to discharge the capacitor into the cell. After the pulse of current the cell terminal voltage should jump up to approx 0.8 to 1V. Stubborn cells may require several repeated zaps before they return to normal voltage. If five or more 'zaps' do not recover the cell it is probably past redemption. When the cell seems to be cleared of the soft short place it on charge at C/10 for 14 hours and measure the terminal voltage. It should be above 1.4V if the cell is recovered. Several charge / discharge cycles are normally needed to bring the capacity back to nominal.

Nickel Cadmium cell rejuvenator

This circuit is one I built to assess the different charging methods for Ni-Cd cells. I first came across this idea in an application note by Westinghouse Electronics in the 1980s. Westinghouse claims that this charging method can rejuvenate tired Ni-Cd cells and return them to near 100% capacity. I found that with the average cells we were using for hand-held two-way radios we could normally attain 90% capacity from cells that would normally be scrapped due to low capacity. However, if the cell has been persistently over charged and gassing occurs, the loss of electrolyte means the cell is basically scrap and nothing short of replacing the lost electrolyte will cause the cell to recover. Hence, it isn't guaranteed to work with all cells.

The principle of the rejuvenator is charging the cell with a much larger current than normal, typically five times the normal rate, and the charger rapidly alternates between charging and discharging. If the majority of the energy pumped into the cell during charging is almost immediately extracted by placing a load across the cell the net charge is quite low. The repetitive charging and discharging claims to 'shake up the chemicals' and give a beneficial result. Westinghouse calls this 'pulse-charging'.

Typically we could charge at C/2 and discharge at C/4, so the net charge retained is only 50%. Westinghouse used a 100% charge and 75% discharge ratio for its tests, hence the energy retained was 25%. This requires an oscillator with a 3:1 pulse width. This technique may not suit all cell types; fast charge cells seem to give lower capacity improvements than normal charge cells from my experience. The indication from experiments is that fast charge cells appear to require charge rates of 5C to 10C to attain the best benefit. For large cells, such as the D-size cells, this is a charging current of about 10 to 20A and a discharge current of 5 to 10A per pulse.

The circuit shown in **Fig 4.15** is dimensioned to suit AA rechargeable cells of 500mAH nominal capacity. The circuit is powered by a 12V / 1A supply. IC1 and IC2 are National Semiconductors LM317 adjustable voltage regulators. IC1 is set up as a conventional voltage regulator to

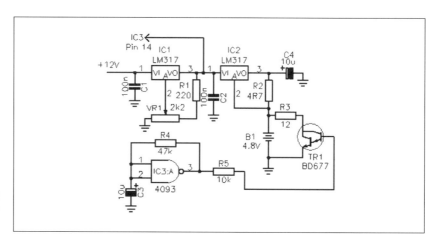

Fig 4.15. Ni-Cd rejuvenator circuit

supply an output voltage approx 2V more than the battery fully charged voltage. This is the 'drop-out' voltage of the LM317 at about 500mA to 1A current. For a four-cell pack this requires approx (4 x 1.5V) + 2V = 8V. IC2 is configured as a constant current source by the resistor in series with the output. The LM317 internal reference voltage between the Output and Adjust pin is 1.25V. With R2 as 4.7Ω the maximum current IC2 can source is 1.25V/4.7Ω = 265mA. This is about five times the normal charge current of an AA cell.

TR1 is a BD677 medium power Darlington NPN transistor (TO-126 package) rated at 4A with a discharge resistor in series with the collector. The current drawn by TR1 when it is turned on is the battery voltage divided by the value of R3, neglecting the saturation voltage of TR1 which is about 0.6V. With the value shown this is approx 4.8 / 12 = 400mA. When TR1 turns on the constant current supplied by IC2 is a portion of the total discharge current. Hence, the actual current being drawn from the battery pack is (400mA - 250mA) = 150mA. This is a value of 3C/10 in terms of battery capacity. Hence, the charging is at 5C/10 and the discharge is at 3C/10. The net charge into the battery is the difference, being 2C/10. Therefore the battery should reach a fully charged state in 14 / 2 hours = 7 hours.

A simple CMOS gate square wave oscillator built around IC3A, which is 1/4 of a CD4093 NAND gate, provides the drive pulse for TR1. This supplies a pulse of approx 1/2s on and 1/2s off with a 50% duty cycle. There may be some advantage is increasing the clock frequency, in which case you can vary the value of R4 or C3. In experiments on various capacity cells a frequency of up to 1kHz was used. Lowering the value of R4 or C3 will increase the frequency. IC3A is powered from the 8V output of IC1.

Resistors R2 and R3 need to be adequately rated, 5W wire-wound types would suit most applications. Similarly IC1, IC2 and TR1 need to be mounted on heatsinks with insulating washers to prevent shorting.

When using this pulse charging technique it is prudent to monitor the cell temperature periodically. If the cells are getting too hot to touch (+50°C or more) this is definitely too hot and the charger should be switched off to allow the cell temperature to fall to ambient. It is also essential to connect a voltmeter across the cells to measure the terminal voltage. If the fully charged voltage is too high the cells will start to gas. Adjust the fully charged voltage with VR1. Connect a voltmeter across R2 and monitor the voltage drop. Disable the discharge transistor TR1 by shorting the base to ground. When the cells are fully charged the voltage across R2 should be close to zero if VR1 has been correctly set.

Negative voltage generator

Some circuits require a negative voltage at a few milli-amps for biasing but only a positive supply is available. Where the current required isn't too high the circuit shown in **Fig 4.16** will perform well. It uses an NE555 multivibrator as a square wave oscillator to generate a negative supply rail. The

Fig 4.16 Negative
supply generator

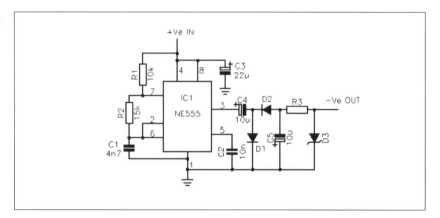

Fig 4.16 Negative
supply generator

frequency of oscillation is approx 5kHz so the output filter capacitor C5 can
be quite a low value. R3 and D3 stabilise the output voltage.

Diodes D1 and D2 can be small signal types such as 1N914 or
1N4148. IC1 switches the positive supply at pin 3 and the rectifier diodes
generate the negative supply. The output voltage is stabilised by D3. R3
should be suitably sized to suit the zener voltage. The voltage rating of C4
needs to be at least twice the positive supply voltage. C5 needs to be rated
at least the positive supply voltage.

Stabilised supply noise filter

For applications that require a very low noise supply, such as the supply
feeding the varicap diode in a voltage controlled oscillator (VCO), the normal zener diode or 3-terminal regulator is often too noisy. A zener diode
can generate a high noise level, something we can use to make a broadband
noise generator. Some 3-terminal regulators also have quite high noise
levels. For a UHF VCO the noise level on the supply rail needs to be very
low. If the tuning rate is 10MHz / volt which is fairly typical for UHF VCOs,
a noise voltage of 10μV on the varicap tuning voltage will generate a residual FM signal of 100Hz.

A simple method is to the use a transistor as a 'capacitor amplifier'.
The circuit shown in **Fig 4.17** uses an NPN transistor to eliminate the noise
riding on the supply and it produces an effective capacitance across the
output terminals, which is a very large value.

Fig 4.17. Low
noise supply
filter

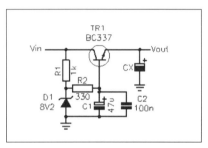

The zener diode D1 supplies the stable DC voltage
from a higher voltage supply rail with R1 as the dropper
resistor. The noise filter consists of R2 and C1 and C2.
This voltage is applied to the base of TR1. The DC output voltage at the emitter of TR1 is approx 0.6V lower
than the voltage supplied by D1 because of the base-
emitter junction voltage drop. (If this is a problem another small signal diode can be inserted in the ground
end of D1 to raise the zener voltage by 0.6V).

The gain of the NPN transistor effectively amplifies the capacitance on the base and a larger capacity CX appears across the output. For the BC337 where the small current gain is approx 400, with C1 at 47µF the value of CX is about 18,800µF. Using a noise filter like the one in Fig 4.17, the residual FM can be lowered by as much as 50dB. The capacitance on the base of TR1 is split into two values. C1 handles the lower frequencies and C2 works better at the higher noise frequencies.

Simple reverse polarity protection

Powering a piece of equipment from a high current power supply or a lead-acid battery requires us to exercise caution when connecting the wires. If the wires are connected the wrong way around substantial damage may occur because of the reverse polarised supply. Some equipment manufacturers fit a reverse polarised diode across the supply input and a series fuse. This causes the fuse to blow if the supply is incorrectly connected. Fuses are a nuisance when this type of reverse polarity protection is used. The way that some two-way radio manufacturers get around this problem is much more effective and the idea was lifted from an old Pye Telecommunications VHF transceiver. This is shown in **Fig 4.18.**

Relay RY is rated for the supply voltage being used. Diode D1 is a small signal diode connected so that the relay coil will only be energised if the supply polarity is correct when the on / off switch SW1 is closed. If the supply is connected incorrectly the relay will not pull in, so preventing the supply being switched through to the equipment. The contacts on the relay need to be rated to carry the equipment current.

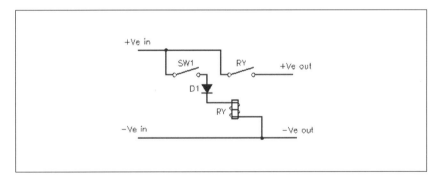

Fig 4.18. Reverse polarity protection

Low voltage step-down converter

Many applications require a lower voltage to be derived from a higher voltage supply rail. A typical application might be a 5V supply to power digital ICs from a nominal 12V supply. For this we could use one of the many 3-terminal regulators, however 'linear regulators' suffer from poor efficiency. They also require a certain minimum input voltage above the required output voltage, the difference being known as the 'dropout' voltage. For most 3-terminal regulators this is about 3V, hence if the input voltage falls below the dropout voltage the output voltage will start to fall. By comparison a switch-mode step-down converter can operate with as little as 1V input-output difference.

If the 3-terminal regulator is supplying a current of 1A with an input voltage of 12V and an output voltage of 5V the power dissipated in the regulator is (12 - 5) x 1A = 7W. Although the output power is only 5W, the total input power is (5 + 7) = 12W, hence the efficiency is 5/12 x 100 = 42%. If the input voltage is 24V the efficiency falls, because the power dissipated in the series pass transistor is now 19W for an output power of 5W. The total efficiency is 5 / 24 x 100 = 21%, or about three times the power being dissipated in the regulator than that being supplied to the load. The input current will always be slightly higher than the output current because the regulator uses some of the input current to power the internal control circuitry, so the efficiency will be slightly worse than the values calculated. The linear regulator is at its most efficient when the input voltage just approaches the dropout point. For a 5V regulator with a 3V-dropout voltage this is with an input voltage of 8V. With an output current of 1A the internal dissipation is 3W and the total input power is 8W, so the efficiency is 5/8 x 100 = 62.5%.

Where the efficiency of the step-down converter is critical, for example in equipment powered by batteries, the use of a switch-mode down converter is the best option. A switch-mode converter can achieve conversion efficiency values of 85% or more whereas a linear regulator is normally about 60% at best. The 25% better efficiency equates to approx 25% more operating time before the battery is exhausted. In fact it can be much more than 25% improvement because the series regulator will drop out when the input voltage reaches approx 2 to 3V above the output voltage. The switch-mode can carry on working until the input to output voltage is as little as 1V or less before the regulator drops out. This can be as much as an extra 20% of battery discharge.

The step-down switch-mode converter is commonly known as a 'Buck Converter'. A simple version can be made that uses the MC34063 IC by On-Semiconductors (previously Motorola). The internal diagram of the MC34063 is shown in **Fig 4.19**.

The MC34063 is capable of operating with an input supply voltage as low as 3V and a maximum of 40V. The DIL version is part number MC34063AP1 rated for 0 to +70°C ambient temperature and the higher specification MC33063AP1 covers the -40 to +85°C temperature range. Several other manufacturers, for example ST-Microelectronics, also make the same IC.

A simple step-down converter is shown in **Fig 4.20** that uses an MC34063 and can supply up to

Fig 4.19. MC34063 internal diagram

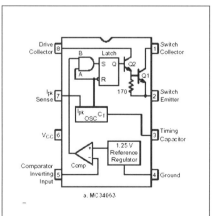

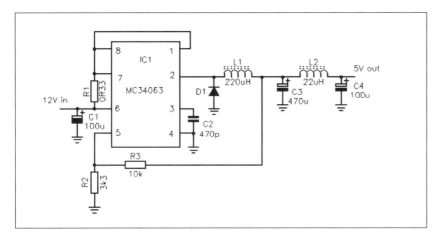

Fig 4.20. 12V to 5V / 500mA Buck Converter

500mA. The benefit of a switch-mode step-down converter is that the current drawn from the input supply is much less than the output current. For a 5V supply powered from a nominal 12V supply the input power is 2.9W at the 500mA output level with an efficiency of 85%. Translating this to the 12V input supply gives an input current of only 245mA. If the input supply were 24V the current required falls to about 125mA.

The switching frequency is set by C2. Resistor R1 in series with the input determines the short circuit current the main switching transistor can draw. Pin 7 is the input to the current limit detector and it monitors the voltage drop between pin 6 and pin 7. If the voltage exceeds 330mV the pulse width of the switching will be reduced to fold back the current. With R1 set as 0.33Ω this will occur when the current reaches 1A. Diode D1 is the recirculation diode, or 'catch-diode', which needs to be a type having a low forward voltage and fast switching. A Schottky diode such as a 1N5819 or an 'Ultra-Fast' diode is the preferred type. Normal rectifiers such as the 1N4002 are not suitable for operation at 100kHz and will cause excessive power dissipation.

Inductors L1 and L2 are wound on powdered iron toroidal cores (see later). Capacitors C1, C3 and C4 should be low ESR types suitable for switch-mode applications. Note: If C1 is a long way from the unregulated supply (lossy wiring etc) this value may need increasing to approx 1000μF. The ESR of the output smoothing capacitor, C3, largely determines the output ripple voltage. An additional filter pole using L2 and C4 reduces the ripple to a low value. The output ripple voltage is approx 10mV, but if a higher ripple voltage is acceptable L2 and C4 can be omitted (without L2 and C4 the ripple voltage will be approx 120mV). The potential divider R2 and R3 feeding the comparison input at pin 5 sets the output voltage. The internal reference voltage is 1.25V. With the values shown the output voltage will be 5.035V. If a different output voltage is required R2 or R3 can be varied in value. The formula to determine the output voltage is:

$$V_{out} = 1.25 \times (1 + \frac{R3}{R2})$$

73

The overall efficiency is determined by several factors, the recirculation diode normally accounts for the bulk of the power dissipated. For a Schottky with a 0.5V forward voltage the power dissipated is the product of V x I, where I is the output current. At 500mA output current the power dissipated is 0.25W. With the assumed efficiency of 85% this is a total of 400mW being dissipated in the various portions of the circuit. Part of the remainder will be dissipated in the series switch transistor and part in the output inductors and capacitors.

Winding details for L1 and L2 using Micrometals Inc cores are:

L1: 82 turns on a T50-26 powdered iron core with 26SWG enamelled copper wire
L2: 26 turns on a T50-26 powdered iron core with 26SWG enamelled copper wire.

Simple add on screen grid stabiliser

The screen grid stabiliser shown earlier is a deluxe version for valves like the 4CX250 series. Often in HF transceivers the output stage consists of 2 x 6JS6C or 6146s. The screen grid supply for these is often very crude and uses simply a resistor from a 300V supply rail. Under varying drive this voltage wanders around. For best intermodulation performance the screen grid voltage needs to be stable. The addition of a few components can achieve better screen grid regulation than the manufacturer's method. The components can be built into the existing output stage with little effort. The only critical item is the heat sinking of the transistor, which needs to have a suitable flat surface and an insulating washer and bush to prevent the collector shorting to ground.

The schematic in **Fig 4.21** shows the details. Resistor R1 is a 5W wire-wound type with a suitable value to drop the 300V supply to approx 175V required by the PA valves. For best regulation the transistor needs to

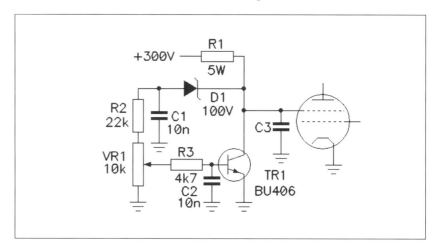

Fig 4.21. Simple screen grid regulator

draw about 50mA. A single 6146 draws a peak screen grid current of about 8mA so for two valves we need to provide a maximum of, say, 20mA worst case under Class-AB1. Hence, for a 300V supply rail a value of about 2k7Ω would be suitable. Zener diode D1 is a 1W type and for most applications 100V will be suitable. R2, R3 and VR1 can be 0.5W types. Capacitors C1 and C2 can be 100V ceramic disc. C3 is the existing screen grid decoupling capacitor. TR1 is a 400V-rated device in a TO-220 package and may be substituted for a number of other types with similar ratings. With a collector current of 50mA and 175V on the collector the power dissipation is approx 9W. The maximum safe collector dissipation of the BU406 is 60W so we are far from its capabilities. Note: TR1 can be replaced with an IRF840 mosfet without any circuit changes.

I modified a Kenwood TS-520 HF transceiver using this circuit. The before and after results were quite striking. The intermodulation distortion products improved by over 10dB at full output. Before modification the screen grid voltage without RF drive was approx +230V and with full drive it fell to around +170V - a 60V change in screen grid voltage, which was terrible.

Although this was bad, the effect it had on the IMD performance was compounded by the way the quiescent current varied. To set the valves' quiescent current the transmitter is keyed up without RF drive and the grid bias voltage adjusted to obtain 60mA anode current (30mA per valve). Under this condition the screen grid voltage is +230V. When driven to full carrier the screen grid voltage drops to +170V. But the real problem is that with no drive the grid bias voltage needs to be quite a bit higher when the screen grid voltage is high. Hence, when the screen grid voltage falls the valves are being pushed more into Class-B than the intended Class-AB1. This requires more drive and also degrades the IMD performance.

Not only does the screen grid voltage vary due to the screen grid current being drawn on speech peaks or keying, the nominal +300V supply also varies by about 45V because it is also feeding the anode of the driver valve, the anode current of which also varies. This is fairly typical of commercially-manufactured amateur HF transceivers and seemingly not of much concern to the designers or manufacturers. If the HF transceiver is driving an additional linear amplifier the overall IMD performance falls to low figures and will generate excessive adjacent channel splatter.

The valve manufacturer recommended screen grid voltage is +150V to +200V with a maximum of +250V, when used in Class-AB1. A voltage of about +175V to +200V is a good compromise. At the higher screen grid voltage we need more grid bias to obtain the correct quiescent anode current. In the manual for the TS-520, Kenwood gives the typical screen grid voltage under receive and transmit conditions. During receive when the valves are biased off with a high grid bias voltage the screen grid voltage is +246V and during transmit the voltage is given as +208V. For best IMD performance the screen grid voltage should be constant, within 100mV preferably.

The driver valve will also be a good candidate for a similar screen grid regulator. Kenwood gives the screen grid voltage of the 12BY7A driver valve as being +236V on receive and +180V during transmit, a variation of about 50V, which is excessive. My example showed greater variations under these conditions. The nominal +300V supply rail varied between approx +370V and as little as +290V under full load. The screen grid voltage for the 12BY7A is derived from a nominal supply rail of +210V, which in my example was closer to +250V. In this case the +175V from the new screen grid regulator could also be fed to the driver valve, improving the overall IMD performance. General Electric data for the 12BY7A valve gives an absolute maximum screen grid voltage of +180V and recommends this figure should not be exceeded for best valve life.

Because IMD degradation is cumulative, the driver stage needs to be approx 6dB better than the figure required from the final stage. If we require an overall IMD figure of -30dBc, the driver should not exceed -36dBc to attain this figure. If using an additional linear amplifier everything has to move back by one stage, the transceiver PA needs to be at worst case -36dBc and the driver stage -42dBc to attain the overall -30dBc for the entire transmitter line-up. This means the stage preceding the driver now needs to be at -48dBc to achieve the required IMD levels.

CHAPTER 5

Test equipment

In this chapter:

- Radio Frequency diode probe
- RF noise head
- Simple pulsed DC supply for a noise head
- An automatic Noise Figure meter
- Infrared tester
- Wideband pulse generator
- Pip-squeak transmitter
- 455kHz marker
- 10.7 and 21.4MHz marker
- Sensitive RF 'sniffer'
- Power supply transient tester
- Deluxe transient tester
- Audio two-tone test oscillator
- 'El cheapo' signal generator
- Saw tooth wave generator
- Broadband RF power meter
- Wide band audio level meter

 OU CAN NEVER have too much test equipment, so here are some circuits I have collected or developed over the years to assist me in constructing amateur equipment.

Radio Frequency diode probe

For measuring small RF voltages in circuit we can use a handheld probe connected to a multi-meter. An item like this is especially useful when first aligning a tuned circuit such as an oscillator or frequency multiplier in an oscillator chain. The normal RF diode probe consists of two small signal

Fig 5.1. Simple
RF diode probe

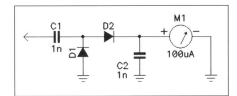

diodes and a few components. The circuit of a typical RF diode probe is shown in **Fig 5.1**.

D1 and D2 are small signal diodes such as 1N4148 or 1N914 although Schottky diodes such as the 1N5711 will give better sensitivity. (Some semiconductor manufacturers make a dual diode in TO92 or SOT-23 packages that are ideal for this application, the BAV99 by Vishay being a good choice). C1 is typically a low value capacitor of about 10pF to 1nF. C2 is a RF decoupling capacitor of about 1nF. The meter should be a sensitive moving coil type of about 50 to 100µA.

The problem with this circuit is that it isn't able to measure very small RF voltages and the loading the probe causes may detune the circuit, so giving a false result. (On negative half cycles the diode D1 appears as a short circuit across the input). A better circuit is shown in **Fig 5.2**. Here a junction FET (JFET) is used in a source follower configuration as a wide band amplifier to buffer the input signal and to transform the high input impedance into a low impedance suitable to drive rectifier diodes. The JFET has a voltage gain of 1 but a medium power gain.

The input loading of the circuit being measured is almost zero because the input coupling capacitor is a very small value. The typical gate to source capacity of an RF JFET is of the order of 2pF, so the total circuit loading is less than 1pF in series with 100kΩ. The value of R2 may need optimising due to the wide variation in pinch-off voltage of the JFET. For best sensitivity and the widest bandwidth the diodes should be 1N5711 or similar. The J-310 or the SMD version, MMBF-310, will work up to about 500MHz at full sensitivity and at least 1GHz with a slightly reduced sensitivity. The circuit can be powered from a small radio battery as the current drawn is only about 10mA.

Fig   5.2.
Improved diode
probe

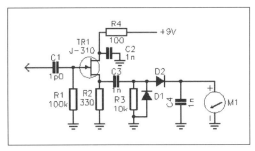

RF noise head

For adjustments to sensitive receivers or low noise amplifiers, a broadband RF noise source is a useful item. One of the devices we can use to generate a wide band noise spectrum is a zener diode, but a good one needs to be selected from a batch. Zener diodes have a rather limited bandwidth and may show much greater output at low frequencies and a dramatic drop off as the frequency increases. The circuit shown in **Fig 5.3** generates a high level of noise over a wide bandwidth and can be used with a noise figure measuring system. The transistor is a general purpose RF NPN type. Many other transistors will work in this circuit, from the humble 2N2222 up to exotic microwave transistors. Whilst experimenting with many different types there was no significant improvement when a microwave transistor was used and the BFW92A shown gave similar results. With a 2N2222 the noise power falls off above about 1GHz, with the BFW92A the noise power is flat to within 0.5dB from 10MHz to over 3GHz. An exotic microwave transistor was only about 0.1dB better up to 3GHz.

For optimum performance and widest bandwidth the circuit could be built using SMD components. The bandwidth with normal leaded components will be slightly less than with SMD components due to the higher lead inductance, but it should still cover up to 2GHz. The transistor is operated in reverse bias mode and the pulsed DC supply needs to be 8V or more, up to about 20V maximum. The output level with 8V applied is about 25dB ENR (excess noise ratio) above a 50Ω resistor at ambient temperature. The transistor feeds a 10dB attenuator to terminate correctly the receiver or low noise amplifier being tested. Hence, the ENR is about 15dB. The output connector should be a low loss type such as an N-type or SMA for the best bandwidth. The pulsed DC connector can be anything from a BNC to a phono connector (RCA).

The following circuit shows the pulsed DC supply for the simple noise head.

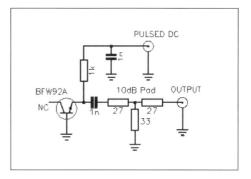

Fig 5.3. Broadband RF noise generator

Simple pulsed DC supply for a noise head

When making adjustments to receivers or low noise amplifiers it is beneficial to use a pulsed source of noise. The human ear is not very good at detecting small changes in noise level but if the noise signal is pulsed on and off at about 15Hz it can detect the difference much better.

The circuit shown in **Fig 5.4** is a single logic gate oscillator and uses only two components to generate a square wave suitable to drive the noise head.

This square wave oscillator is about as simple as you can get. The CD4093 is a quad NAND gate with a Schmidt trigger input. The cost is low and you get four gates in one 14-pin DIL package. Normal CD4000 series CMOS logic gates will operate on a supply voltage of 3V to 15V. R1 and C1 set the frequency. The formula to determine the oscillator period, and hence the frequency, is T = 0.7 x RC, where R is in ohms and C is in Farads. With the values shown the time constant T is 100ms and hence the frequency is 1/T = 14Hz. The output signal is a square wave swinging between ground and the IC supply rail. If the IC is powered from a 9V supply the output will swing to 8.4V. Although the gate cannot source very much current it is adequate because TR1 buffers the output and gives a low impedance output to drive the noise head.

Fig 5.4. Single gate square wave oscillator

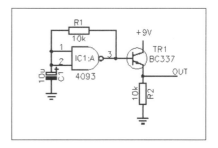

An automatic Noise Figure meter

For amateurs requiring a better method of indicating Noise Figure when aligning a receiver or LNA the design that follows gives good results and allows the Noise Figure to be set to the lowest possible. In actual fact this design does not measure Noise Figure; but instead indicates when the lowest Noise Figure has been achieved.

The schematic is split into two parts due to the problems of printing a large diagram with sufficient resolution. The first half of the schematic shows the pulse generator and audio processing stages. If **Fig 5.5** and **Fig 5.6** are placed side by side the connection between the two circuits will be obvious.

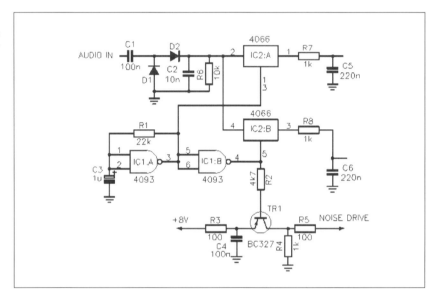

Fig 5.5. Noise Figure meter pulse generator and audio stages

The square wave oscillator uses one CD4093 gate, a second gate is used to provide an inverted signal. The oscillator runs at approx 50Hz. The two square wave signals are 180° out of phase and drive the control pins of two CD4066 analog switches. The square wave signal is also used to turn on and off the pulsed DC supply to the Noise Head via TR1.

The audio from the receiver is rectified in D1 and D2 and the resulting DC voltage is stored on C2. The two CD4066 switches connect the rectified audio signal alternatively. When the noise head is powered up, generating the broadband noise, analog switch IC2A is closed and sends the corresponding noise voltage to R7 and the filter capacitor C5. When the noise head is turned off, analog switch IC2B will be closed and the corresponding DC signal is sent to R8 and C6. The DC voltages stored on C5 and C6 are directly in a ratio to the noise signal difference. The greater the difference in voltage between these two conditions the more sensitive the receiver. These voltages are then processed in the circuit shown in Fig 5.6.

The DC amplifier takes the two DC signals and a *differential ampli-*

fier generates a DC voltage that is proportional to the difference between the two signals. (IC3A connects to C5 and IC3B connects to C6). The resulting DC voltage is further amplified in IC4A and used to drive a 1mA moving coil meter to display the Noise Figure. VR1 allows the meter sensitivity to be set.

In use the receiver is set to AM or SSB and the RF gain control set to maximum. The audio input for the meter is made by connecting to the headphones jack socket. Adjust the AF gain control until the meter indicates approximately half scale. By adjusting the LNA or receiver input circuits the meter reading will increase as the noise figure or sensitivity is improved. Hence, all you need to do is to tune for maximum meter indication.

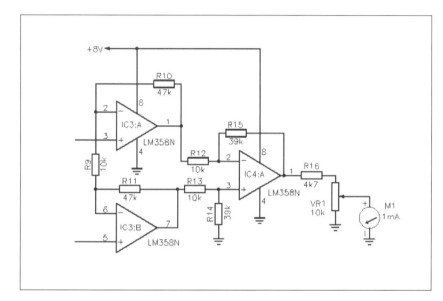

Fig 5.6. DC amplifier for the Noise Figure meter

Infrared tester

Infrared emitters and detectors are used in a large number of domestic appliances and computer equipment. Because the human eye cannot see the infrared spectrum we need a detector to tell if a device is working correctly. The circuit shown in **Fig 5.7** is an *infrared link* using an LED and an Opto-transistor sensitive to IR.

The infrared emitting LED transmitter (D1) is pulsed with a square wave current generated by IC1A and amplified by TR1. The frequency is approx 100Hz. The infrared receiver (TR2) is an Opto-transistor. The output of TR2 is fed to an emitter follower (TR3) and used to drive a small 300Ω speaker. If the transmitter and receiver are working, a 100Hz buzzing noise should be heard in LS1. By placing an opaque material between the two devices the transmission can be interrupted. The maximum distance between the two IR devices should not exceed 100mm for best results.

81

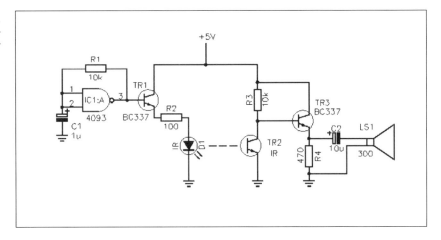

This circuit can also be used to test remote controls for televisions and car remote locking by pointing the remote at the Opto-transistor and listening to the receiver speaker. If the remote is working, the speaker should reproduce the pulse code modulation audibly. If an oscilloscope is connected across R4 and the speaker disconnected the waveform can be viewed.

Wideband pulse generator

For adjusting items such as a noise blanker we need a signal to inject into the receiver that closely represents the ignition interference produced by an internal combustion engine. The circuit shown in **Fig 5.8** delivers very narrow pulses which are of a high amplitude. The circuit is built around the ubiquitous NE555 timer IC.

Capacitor C1 alternatively charges via TR1 and is then discharged rapidly when the voltage across C1 exceeds the threshold on pin 2 of the 555. When this occurs, the timer IC discharges C1 in almost zero time. This develops very high amplitude spikes at the output. The time between the spikes is determined by the value of resistor R2. With a value of 1MΩ spikes occur every 100ms.

Fig 5.8. Narrow pulse generator

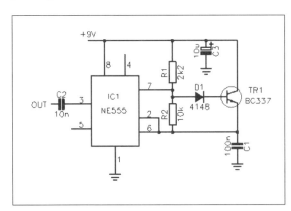

The output should be connected to the receiver input with a piece of coax cable because the signal level drops off at very high frequencies. At low frequencies an attenuator may be required to prevent saturating the receiver by the high amplitude pulses. A 1kΩ pot connected from the output of C2 to ground can be used to vary the amplitude of the signal, the signal from the pot being taken from the slider via the coax cable to the receiver input.

Another application for this circuit is to generate time 'marker pips' on an oscilloscope time base sweep. By coupling into the Y input in parallel with a signal being measured the spikes will appear as narrow blips on the trace being displayed.

Pip-squeak transmitter

This circuit is one I built many years ago to assist in aligning a 23cm converter. Often we require a fairly weak signal to align a receiving converter but can never find a signal on the band when we need one. This circuit generates a fairly strong signal for initial alignment (approx -90dBm) when connected by a short coax cable to the converter. By fitting a small whip antenna it can be placed some distance away for final alignment using the station antenna. A small transistor radio battery powers the signal source. I have used this signal source up to 1km away from the station and the signal is easy to find on a sensitive receiver.

The oscillator uses a third overtone crystal and the oscillator drives a diode multiplier. The half wave tuned line selects the required harmonic. The tuned line is a piece of brass or copper strip 0.5mm to 1mm thick (shim stock) that measures 50mm long and 6mm wide. The two ends are bent down so the line is approx 6mm above the ground plane and looks like an extended U shape upside down. (The length of the line before it is bent is about 62mm). The tapping point for the diode and output are made at 10mm from each end. The tuning capacitor is a Philips tubular trimmer bolted to the ground plane and standing vertically. The line is soldered to the trimmer at the centre of the line.

With the 27MHz crystal the signal output is at 1296.00MHz as the 48th harmonic is selected. By changing the output tuned circuit the signal source will also generate a signal on 432MHz using the 16th harmonic. Set the oscillator on to the correct frequency by listening to the 27MHz signal on a short-wave receiver and adjusting the trimmer in series with the crystal to zero beat it against the receiver's 100kHz calibrator.

Although the circuit shows a BFY90 transistor, which today is a rare device, many modern devices will work. A device I regularly use is the

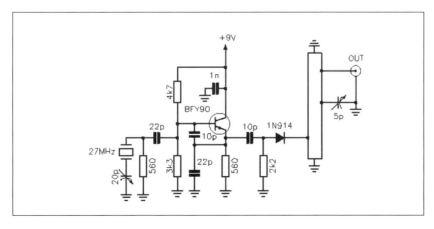

Fig 5.9. Alignment signal source

Fig 5.10. A signal source for 144MHz

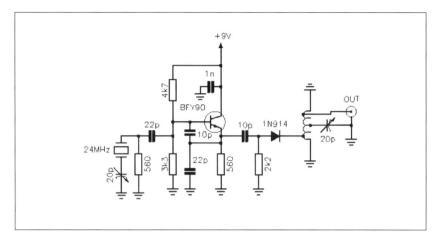

Fig 5.10. A signal source for 144MHz

MPSH-10 in the TO-92 package. A version suitable for 144MHz is shown in **Fig 5.10**. This uses a 24MHz crystal and so will suit 432MHz as well by changing the output tank circuit inductor.

The output tank inductor consists of six turns of 20SWG tin copper wire wound on a 6mm former and is self-supporting by soldering the two ends of the inductor to the ground plane. The coil is spread so the turns are about a wire diameter apart. The tapping points for the diode and output are one turn from each ground point. The tuning capacitor is a 20pF plastic film trimmer. The output level from this signal source is strong, over S9 on the average receiver, and so an attenuator will need to be used between it and the receiver to prevent over loading.

455kHz marker

When aligning a receiver that uses a 455kHz IF, a marker generator is a very useful piece of equipment. If a 455kHz marker output is placed close to the IF circuit and the receiver is receiving an unmodulated carrier, either from an accurate signal generator or the local repeater, a beat note will be heard. By adjusting the receiver 1st LO crystal the beat note can be brought to zero frequency. This is the way two-way radio workshops set up the LO and this method cancels out any error in the 2nd LO used to convert from 10.7MHz or 21.4MHz to the final IF at 455kHz. This method works equally well for AM or FM receivers and is a quick and accurate method of setting the receiver 1st LO on frequency.

The transistor used for the oscillator is not especially critical; almost any audio NPN transistor will work at this low frequency. The crystal can be either a real crystal or a ceramic

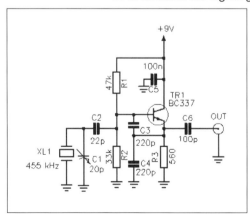

Fig 5.11. 455kHz marker

resonator. For the lowest cost the ceramic resonator is the best option. The circuit is built into a small box and a connector such as a banana socket and plug allows a short piece of insulated wire to be dangled near the 2nd IF circuitry. The coupling between the IF and the wire needs to be quite loose if the receiver is a FM type or the 455kHz signal will cause excessive quieting of the IF. I built it into a small plastic box that contained a PP3 battery and a push button switch to turn on the marker when required. The output connector is a phono socket (RCA) and the matching plug has a short piece of 1.6mm brazing rod soldered in and covered with heatshrink sleeving. By holding the end of the whip antenna near the IF and pressing the button the beat note can be heard.

10.7 and 21.4MHz marker

The idea for the 455kHz marker can also be used to generate a stable marker for the popular IFs of 10.7 and 21.4MHz. As you may have noticed, these are harmonically related, 21.4MHz being exactly twice 10.7MHz. Hence by using a 10.7MHz crystal we can get both signals from one unit.

The BC337 will work fine at 10.7MHz although some might prefer a 'real' RF transistor. In this case an MPSH-10 will deliver a larger signal. Again a short whip antenna can be used to couple into the circuit under test. 10.7MHz crystals are expensive to buy in one-off quantities but an old crystal filter will contain as many as six or more close tolerance crystals. The old Pye Westminster two-way radios contain a nice 10.7MHz filter and these can sometimes be found at mobile rallies for very little outlay. By carefully unsoldering the can and extracting a crystal it can be used and pulled on to frequency with the trimmer.

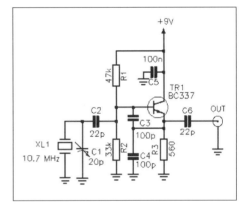

Fig 5.12. 10.7 and 21.4MHz marker

Sensitive RF 'sniffer'

When aligning an item of RF circuitry it is useful to be able to see the level of the signal as the circuit is adjusted. In most cases an absorption wave-meter can be used, but for some circuits the wave-meter coil is too big to get close enough to obtain a good indication. In professional RF design laboratories one often finds an item known as a 'sniffer'. This is a small coil of about two turns wound with enamelled copper wire and attached to the end of a piece of 50Ω coax which is connected to a spectrum analyser. By moving this around the equipment, points of maximum RF can be found. Often the sniffer is used to examine the shielding effectiveness, as slots or holes in equipment leak RF that can be detrimental to other pieces of equipment. The measurement obtained is not highly accurate but by comparing

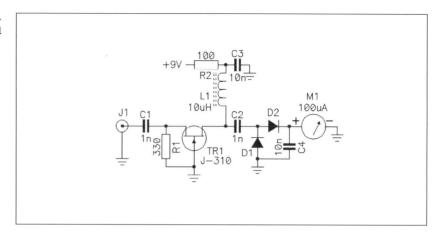

Fig 5.13. Sensitive wideband RF 'sniffer'

the results to other points in the equipment a good indication of the problem can be reached.

The circuit shown in **Fig 5.13** is a wideband RF amplifier that drives a rectifier and the amplitude of the signal is shown on the moving coil meter. The JFET is operated in grounded gate for maximum stability and the input signal coupled into the source. The amplified signal at the drain is detected by the diodes D1 and D2 and the amplitude is shown on the meter. For best sensitivity the diodes can be Schottky such as the 1N5711. 1N914 or 1N4148 diodes will give slightly lower sensitivity. The drain inductor should be a small molded choke. If instability is observed, a resistor in parallel with L1 will reduce the tendency to oscillation when the input is mismatched. A good starting point is 1kΩ. Ensure the gate lead is as short as possible to reduce the chances of instability. For best results the circuit should be built into a metal enclosure to exclude any stray RF signals.

The sniffer probe is two turns of enamelled copper wire wound on a 6 to 8mm former and the coil is soldered across the end of a piece of 50Ω coax cable. The other end of the cable has a suitable RF connector (BNC) and connects to the amplifier unit. Alternatively solder the coils to BNC connectors.

By replacing the sniffer coil with a short whip antenna the unit becomes a sensitive RF field strength meter. With a quarter-wave whip cut to 144MHz the unit indicates reliably up to 10m from a mobile radiating 10W into a 5/8-wave whip.

Fig 5.14. Two RF sniffer probes mounted on BNC connectors

Power supply transient tester

When constructing a linear regulated power supply it is prudent to perform some testing before using it to power an expensive piece of equipment. Many power supplies are not well designed and this can cause problems if something goes wrong. Most amateurs are not aware of the necessity of performing a transient test to see if the supply can handle sudden changes in current demand. If the loop-stability is not what it should be the power supply can cause damage to the attached equipment.

What we need is a piece of test equipment that can vary the current drawn rapidly between two conditions, typically about 10% of the maximum and 100% of the maximum. The quicker this can be achieved the easier it is to see the transient over shoot or under shoot as the current level is varied.

Why is transient testing so important?

If we take the analogy of a motor vehicle with worn shock absorbers we can draw a parallel case. In a motor vehicle with worn shock absorbers the wheel and tyre are not in contact with the road surface all the time. If the wheel runs over a bump the sudden upwards movement causes the tyre to lose contact with the road. The spring will eventually return the wheel to the road surface by releasing the energy stored in it. But if a second bump occurs before the wheel has stopped bouncing the driver may lose control of the vehicle. In a vehicle with good shock absorbers the wheel is returned to a stable condition quickly. This is known as a *critically damped response*. The worn shock absorber is an *under damped response*.

Power supplies behave in a similar way. If the current being drawn is rapidly varying, and a typical case is when we transmit on CW or SSB, the under damped condition can allow a high voltage to appear across the output when the load current is suddenly reduced from key down to key up. If the transient stability is not good then there may be a big bang as the attached equipment experiences a sudden over voltage condition.

Testing a power supply with fixed load currents doesn't exercise the supply in a way to induce transients. So it may well be that although it seems to be a good power supply the acid test is to subject it to a transient test before using it to power an expensive transceiver.

The first circuit (**Fig 5.15**) is the very simple version that will at least be able to tell us if we need to look any closer. This uses two high power resistors that are sized to draw 10% of the maximum and 90% of the maximum. The 10% load resistor (R3) is permanently connected across the power supply under investigation. The second resistor (R2) is switched into and out of circuit by a hefty power transistor. A square wave oscillator performs the switching.

The resistor values shown suit a 13.8V supply of about 10A. R2 is sized to

Fig 5.15. Basic transient tester

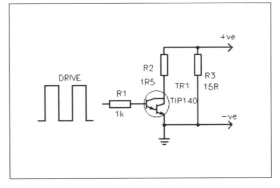

draw 90% of the current, when both are in circuit this is 100% load current. R2 is made up of 10 x 15Ω wire-wound resistors connected in parallel. R3 is another 15Ω resistor. The resistors used must be able to dissipate safely the anticipated power. In this example the resistors are rated at 15W minimum. R3 will be dissipating 9.2W continuously. R2 will be dissipating 127W with a 50% duty cycle and so we need a minimum of a 65W resistor. 10 x 15W resistors = 150W so this will be safe.

TR1 is a large NPN Darlington that can safely handle10A if correctly heatsinked; the official rating is 125W on a good heatsink. In this application the bulk of the dissipation is occurring in R2 and TR1 will only be dissipating about 30W at the 9.2A collector current. This is determined by the collector saturation voltage; the manufacturer gives a maximum value of 3V at 10A.

The drive signal is obtained from a square wave oscillator capable of driving the TIP140 into saturation. The current gain of the TIP140 is approx 1000 so the oscillator needs to be able to source 10mA of drive minimum. An op-amp square wave oscillator can deliver up to 30mA into a short circuit so this would suit the bill nicely.

With the transient tester hooked up to the power supply, before switching on connect an oscilloscope probe across the supply terminals. Set the 'scope to AC coupling, as we need to observe the peak-peak transient. Now switch on the supply and enable the transient tester drive. Sweep the frequency of the square wave oscillator slowly from about 10Hz to about 400Hz, this being the area where problems normally occur.

Examine the transient waveform for any large changes in output voltage. If a voltage of more than 1V pk-pk is seen then you have some work to do to fix the problem. A good power supply will show less than 100mV pk-pk transient induced voltage.

If prolonged testing is needed a small 12V fan can be used to blow air across the heatsink and the load resistors to keep the temperature low.

Deluxe transient tester

The first design is something we can build in an evening. The next design is a bit more complex but has some features the first design doesn't have. These include being able to vary continuously the idle current and the peak current whilst being modulated with a transient test pulse. The circuit is shown in **Fig 5.16**.

This is a continuously variable 'current sink' which can also be modulated. In the unmodulated state it allows the current drawn to be varied between practically zero and the maximum. Once the current being drawn has been set the current remains constant even if the power supply output voltage should vary.

The maximum current is determined by the load transistors and the tail resistors R6, R7 and R8. The values shown suit a 10 to 15A supply. The load transistors are TIP140 and two are connected in parallel giving a safe maximum current of about 20A. The difference between this circuit and the previous one is that here almost all the power is dissipated in the load

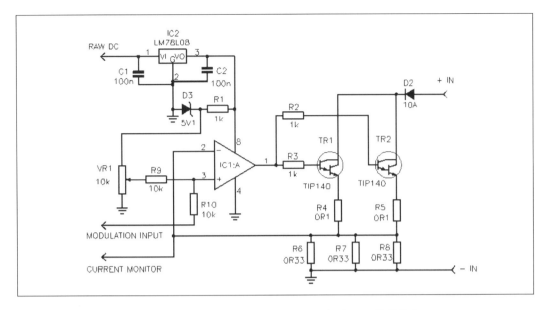

Fig 5.16. Deluxe transient tester

transistors, so the heatsinking needs to be very good. A small DC fan blowing on to the heatsink is a good addition if extended testing is required. R4 to R8 are 5W wire wound resistors. R4 and R5 are 0.1Ω / 5W current sharing resistors and force each transistor to draw equal current. R6 to R8 are 0.33Ω / 5W resistors connected in parallel. These can be replaced by a single 0.1Ω / 15W resistor if available.

The current drawn is controlled by IC1A, which is half of a dual op-amp. An LM358N was used. VR1 sets the current to the desired level. This should be a multi-turn panel mount pot if possible to allow fine setting. IC1 requires a stable supply and an LM78L08 (IC2) is used to power the circuit. This is derived from a 12V internal supply with a small transformer and bridge rectifier / capacitor. The diode in series with the input (D2) is to protect the load transistors from reverse polarity. It should be a low forward voltage diode such as a Schottky in a TO-220 package and well heatsinked and rated at 20A or so. D2 can be omitted if you are certain you will always connect the load wires correctly.

The modulation circuitry is shown in **Fig 5.17**.

IC3A is a NAND gate oscillator using a CD4093. The frequency is varied by VR2. With the component values shown the oscillator can be varied between 2Hz and 100Hz. By switching different capacitors for C3 it can be set to any desired frequency. The amplitude of the pulse is controlled by VR3. The variable amplitude pulse is buffered in the voltage follower IC1B, the second half of the LM358N. Current metering is performed by monitoring the tail resistor voltage, and M1 displays the average current being drawn. SKT1 allows a 'scope to be connected to measure the transient current visually.

To use as an unmodulated current sink VR3 is set to zero and VR1 is adjusted to give the required current load. Using this the voltage regulation can be measured with a DVM connected across the power supply

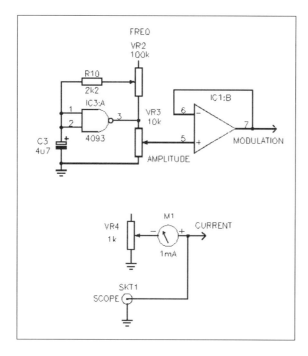

output terminals for different load currents.

For transient testing the required minimum current is set by VR1. Next VR3 is adjusted to pulse the current to the required peak amplitude. The frequency can be swept by varying VR2. The transient current waveform via SKT1 is observed on the connected 'scope.

When observing the output voltage of the supply under test with an AC coupled 'scope, the 'scope waveform will show very narrow spikes caused by the rapid switching. These are not normally a problem. These can in some cases be as large as 2V but are of very short duration (typically about 10µs) and normally will not cause a problem. These are not generated in the power supply but in the load transistors by stored charge in the collector-emitter junction. The power supply will not see these because of the low

Fig 5.17. Modulation circuit

frequency cut off in the servo loop control circuit.

What we are looking for are extended periods where the output voltage remains higher than the nominal voltage. Also any oscillatory ringing, which normally occurs when the servo loop is unstable, will be evident if the power supply has a serious problem. All regulated power supplies exhibit this effect to some degree because the control circuitry requires a finite time to return the output voltage to normal when the current is suddenly reduced. This is because the servo loop cut off frequency is normally quite low, typically less than 50Hz to eliminate the mains ripple from the reservoir capacitor. The low frequency cut off in the servo loop means that any pulsing current at frequencies above about 50Hz will be out of the control loop and the servo control will effectively be running open-loop at frequencies higher than 50Hz. Hence, it is normal to see quite large load induced voltage dips at frequencies above about 50Hz. Below about 20Hz the loop should compensate and turn up the pass transistor drive to smooth these out. It is around the transition frequency where oscillatory problems are most common due to insufficient gain and phase compensation.

A similar condition occurs with an internal combustion engine. If you press down on the accelerator pedal with the transmission in neutral the engine speed will rise. If you now lift off the pedal the engine does not return to idle immediately because the kinetic energy stored in the mass of the flywheel only allows the speed to fall slowly. This is a critically damped response.

The opposite case occurs when the load is switched from the idle value to maximum. A load induced dip in output voltage is perfectly normal and as long as the servo-loop control circuit in the power supply corrects the problem in a critically damped manner there is nothing to worry about. Below the loop cut off frequency the load induced voltage dip should be corrected; above it the loop does not know it has occurred and so the dip will extend as long as the pulse duration. Again it is the manner in which the output voltage returns to normal that is the most important factor.

For the open-loop load induced voltage dip the only thing able to correct this is the charge stored in the output capacitor fitted across the supply terminals. This capacitor must not be too high a value, because it also holds up the output voltage when the load current is reduced from maximum to minimum. In this condition the pass transistors are turned on fairly hard, when the load suddenly reduces the output capacitor will start charging up to a higher than normal voltage and may exceed the safe voltage of the attached equipment before the servo loop can back off the pass transistors drive.

Audio two-tone test oscillator

When adjusting SSB transmitters for best linearity a common technique is to use a two-tone audio oscillator. By injecting into the microphone socket two equal amplitude sinusoidal tones separated by a small frequency difference the intermodulation performance can be assessed. For optimum measurement a spectrum analyser is required to measure the IMD products. However, an oscilloscope detecting the RF envelope can also tell us a lot about how the transmitter is performing.

The circuit of a high purity sine wave oscillator is shown in **Fig 5.18**. This uses a phase shift network between the output and the input to set the oscillator frequency.

The high pass network consisting of C2, R6, R7 and R8 sets the frequency. The capacitors used for C2 need to be close tolerance types and preferably selected to find four capacitors within 2% or better. Polycarbonate or polyester capacitors are the best choice. Similarly the resistors need to be closely matched and 2% types would be the best

Fig 5.18. Sine wave audio oscillator

choice. The values shown for R6 to R8 are for the 1kHz oscillator. The second oscillator is identical except R6 to R8 need to be lower in value to set the high tone to approx 1.8kHz. For 1.8kHz the value of R6 to R8 is 39kΩ. The two tones used must not be harmonically related, so 1kHz and 2kHz are not acceptable. Also important is that the higher frequency tone must fall within the pass band of the SSB filter, which normally limits the high tone to lower than 2.5kHz.

The two oscillators are connected together with a resistive combiner fea-

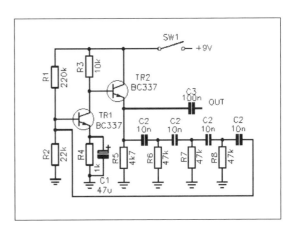

91

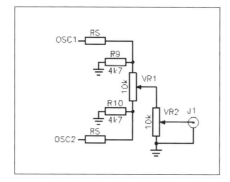

Fig 5.19. Signal combiner and output level control

turing a balance control and an output setting control. This is shown in **Fig 5.19**. If the output voltage is too much a resistor (RS) can be inserted between each oscillator output and VR1 to reduce the level. Most SSB transmitters only require about 100mV to drive them to full output.

VR1 is a balance control to set the two-tone amplitudes to be the same value. VR2 sets the level of the composite two-tone signal to the transmitter microphone input. Either oscillator may be used independently by switching off the unwanted oscillator. The circuit should be enclosed in a well-shielded box to prevent RF from the transmitter upsetting the performance. Similarly the output lead to the microphone connector should be a screened cable.

To set up the circuit first switch off one of the oscillators and measure the signal from the active oscillator at the slider of VR1 when it is exactly at mid travel, note the level in mV AC. Switch the second oscillator on and the first one off and repeat the measurement. If an imbalance exists adjust VR1 so that the two measurements are the same. Having set VR1 do not change the position. Now switch on both oscillators and measure the resulting rms AC signal at VR1 slider. This should increase in value by 1.414 if the two signals are the same amplitude.

If an oscilloscope is available observing the relative peak amplitudes on the trace will give a more accurate setting. The trace when the timebase is fairly slow should look like a 100% modulated AM carrier waveform. The envelope should just fall to zero at the crossing point. If an amplitude imbalance exists the waveform will look like an AM carrier that is not fully modulated or over modulated.

When the two-tone oscillator is connected to an SSB transmitter the RF envelope should look like the 100% AM carrier. The best method is to drive the transmitter into a good dummy load and tap off a small sample of RF to feed into the oscilloscope Y amplifier. (If the 'scope does not have a high enough operating bandwidth, such as is the case for VHF or UHF transmitters, a detector diode can be used to derive a sample of the modulation, see **Fig 5.20**). Advance VR2 until the RF envelope reaches maximum deflection and observe the envelope shape. Over driving will cause the top of the envelope to flatten out. The RF wattmeter will show an average reading of 50% of the peak envelope power. So if the transmitter is rated at 100W PEP do not expect any more than 50W average. If the envelope begins flattening before the 50W average power is reached, that is the maximum linear power the transmitter is capable of and the microphone gain control and RF drive control should be set so the envelope shows a clean sine wave envelope.

For a more accurate measurement we can use each tone independently. Start with one tone and adjust the level to achieve exactly 25% of the PEP rating of the transmitter. Switch off the first tone and switch on the

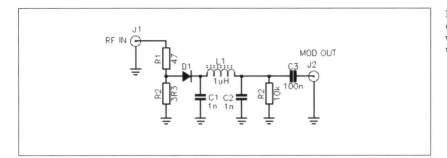

Fig 5.20. 50Ω dummy load with modulation sampler

second tone. The indicated power should also be 25% of the PEP rating. With both tones switched on the indicated average power should increase to exactly 50%. Having set the power observe the carrier envelope on the 'scope and ensure it is a clean 100% modulated AM carrier.

'El cheapo' signal generator

There is an interesting tale about this item. This was my first signal generator until I could afford to buy a commercially made item from the government surplus market. In the early 1970s I was building my first 70cm converter but had very little in the way of RF test equipment. My total arsenal consisted of a homemade diode probe, an old and ropy 5MHz bandwidth oscilloscope, a home-brewed frequency counter that counted up to 110MHz and various multi-meters of dubious parentage. Setting the crystal oscillator on the correct frequency was no problem and an absorption wave-meter quickly lashed together allowed the multiplier chain to be brought fairly close to optimum.

When it came to aligning the RF amplifier stages of the 70cm converter I was at a disadvantage compared to amateurs with better equipped shacks. I had tried aligning using the third harmonic of the 2m transmitter but this only resulted in tuning up on the wrong frequency (288MHz). As always happens, when you need a signal on the band there is none to be found! One day on 2m I was talking to an old timer about my dilemma and he told me how to solve the problem.

Take an old biscuit tin and punch a hole in the side to take a RF socket and connect a 47Ω 1/4W resistor across the connector on the inside of the box with fairly long leads. Punch a second hole to take an on / off toggle switch and bolt the switch with the toggle on the outside of the box. With me so far?

Now the clever bit: the *RF generator*. Take an old doorbell and remove the gong and fit it into the box. Place a 4.5V bell battery or a 6V-lantern battery in the box and wire the switch to the doorbell so it vibrates when the switch is closed. Place lid on box and you have a wide band 'hash' generator. The inductive solenoid causes sparks across the contacts of the doorbell and the interference generated is picked up by the *coupling loop* formed by the resistor across the RF connector.

Finally, connect a 70cm bandpass filter in series with the 'signal generator' and the 70cm converter. It so happened I had a band-pass filter from an old UHF Pye Cambridge that fitted the bill OK. So there you have it - a wide-band noise generator, which is band limited by the bandpass filter.

It worked so well I wondered why I had never seen it described before. Fitting an appropriate bandpass filter to suit the band allowed use on many different frequencies, even as high as 23cm. With this little item I was able to align the 70cm converter by listening to the signal on the tunable IF. Moving the doorbell around in the box to place it closer or further away from the pickup loop varies the signal level; crude but effective.

The old timer told me he had several items like this he had made many years ago, one for each band. Each one consisted of a high Q filter and a doorbell in a small tin box. When he needed to check his converter alignment he simply took the appropriate 'generator' off the shelf and clipped a pair of leads on to a battery.

Although this is a very crude method it does have certain advantages. Instead of needing a stable RF carrier and an SSB receiver, by using a wide band noise source and an AM receiver we can quickly swing the tunable IF tuning dial across the band to see if we have similar sensitivity at the bottom and top ends of the band. Often if we align at the band centre the performance will drop off at the band edges.

Saw tooth wave generator

Many items of test equipment require a linear saw tooth generator. The saw tooth waveform sweeps the trace of an oscilloscope or spectrum analyser. The more linear the waveform the more accurate the calibration to the graticule markings. The voltage can also be used to drive a varicap diode in a voltage-controlled oscillator for a sweep generator. A good design for a linear saw tooth generator is shown in **Fig 5.21**.

The capacitor C1 is alternately charged and discharged. TR1 and TR2 are configured as an uni-junction transistor that cause the voltage on C1 to fall to zero in practically zero time when the capacitor is fully charged. TR3 and the potential divider resistors control the linear charging of C1 by a constant current source. Two transistors are connected as diodes to stabilise the potential divider chain for the constant current source. The voltage on C1 is applied to the emitter follower TR6 giving low output impedance.

The frequency of oscillation is determined by the time constant of C1 x R4. For a saw tooth oscillator requiring several different frequencies (sweep speeds) C1 can be switched with a multi-pole switch and R4 made partly variable with a pot in series. C1 should be a low leakage capacitor to maximise the linearity. For long sweep periods the best choice would be a solid tantalum.

Fig 5.21. Saw tooth generator

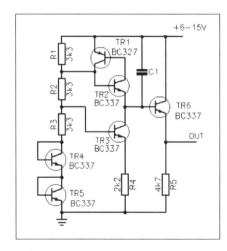

Broadband RF power meter

When we need to measure very low power levels the traditional method is to use an expensive item such as a measuring receiver of a spectrum analyser. Most laboratory power meters such as the HP-432 series are unable to measure power levels lower than about -25dBm. A method that can measure very low power levels uses a wideband logarithmic amplifier. A low cost log-amp is the Analog Devices AD-8307 in an 8-pin DIL or SMD package. This IC will accurately measure power levels from approx -75dBm to +15dBm, a range of 90dB from 10MHz to over 500MHz. Logarithmic amplifiers responds to voltage and not power; the usual types have a high input impedance and so a low value load resistor connected across the input can be used to generate a RF voltage when power is dissipated in it.

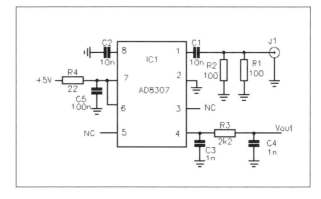

Fig 5.22. Broadband power meter

The circuit of the broadband power meter is shown in **Fig 5.22**. The AD-8307 has two inputs arranged as a differential stage (pins 1 and 8). For a single ended input one of the inputs is AC grounded via a low reactance capacitor (C2). The power to be measured is terminated in a resistive load, this circuit is designed for 50Ω and R1 and R2 connected in parallel across J1 and coupled to the input of the IC by C1. For the best bandwidth the resistors used for R1 and R2 should be low inductance types such as chip resistors.

The AD-8307 requires a stable supply voltage of 2.7 to 5.5V. C3, R3 and C4 filter the detected output at pin 4. This voltage corresponds to the magnitude of the input RF voltage and is essentially flat from 10MHz to at least 500MHz within 2% error. The AD-8307 will work up to 900MHz but the input versus output curve is not as good as at lower frequencies. The typical calibration curves for several frequencies is shown in **Fig 5.23** as supplied by Analog Devices.

Because the AD-8307 has a very high gain (90dB) and a wide bandwidth it is essential to construct the circuit with good RF layout techniques and low inductance decoupling capacitors to prevent instability and to enclose it in a well-shielded box to exclude unwanted RF signals. The optimum capacitors would be surface mount (chip) types.

Fig 5.23. Calibration curves for 10MHz, 100MHz and 500MHz *(used with permission of Analog Devices)*

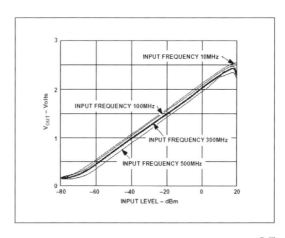

Wide band audio level meter

The circuit above could be reconfigured to make a wide band audio level meter, but the AD8307 is not the cheapest method. In this circuit we will use a Philips Semiconductors FM IF integrated circuit. The NE604 is a normally used for a limiting FM IF at 455kHz and it has a bandwidth of approx 2MHz. An application note from Philips supplied the basis of the circuit.

The circuit in **Fig 5.24** shows the connection method. Audio is supplied to the input of the NE604 at pin 16. The input impedance is high and should not cause excessive loading to a circuit under test. The resistor R1 and capacitor C5 limit the audio bandwidth to about 15kHz. The NE604 contains an accurate RSSI detector that is scaled in a logarithmic format. The maximum output voltage is 5V DC and this corresponds to an audio signal of 300mV p-p at the input. The total RSSI range is approx 80dB. The dual Op-Amp IC2 is an NE5532, also by Philips, and has a low pass filter on the RSSI detected output to smooth out any noise. The maximum supply voltage of the NE604 is 9V, but Philips recommends using 6V.

The NE604 is contained in a 16-pin package and any pins not shown are left floating in this application.

Fig 5.24. Wide band audio level meter

This circuit with a suitable microphone could be used for an audio level meter scaled in dBa to measure sound pressure levels or as a signal tracer for audio equipment.

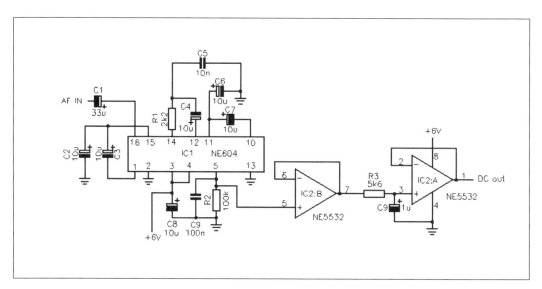

CHAPTER 6

Miscellaneous circuits

In this chapter:

- A simple intercom system
- 'K' generator
- Poor man's Christmas tree light flasher
- Wind speed indicator

HIS CHAPTER includes the circuits that do not fall into any logical section. These are what I might term 'silly circuits' I have developed over the years that may interest some readers.

A simple intercom system

This simple circuit allows communication between two remote points. It isn't actually an 'intercom', as most people understand the term. However, it allows my wife and me to communicate. The shack is some distance from the house in an out building and because of the high incidence of lightning occurring in this country a normal intercom would not last very long. We do, however, have an extension telephone in the shack as this also doubles as the office. The circuit is powered from the 12V standby battery in the shack and allows a form of communication between the 'Domestic Executive' (otherwise known as 'her indoors') and me.

The circuit is shown in **Fig 6.1**. It is really very simple and uses a minimum amount of components. The sounders are self oscillating piezo-electric transducers that emit a loud 'squawk' when supplied with a voltage.

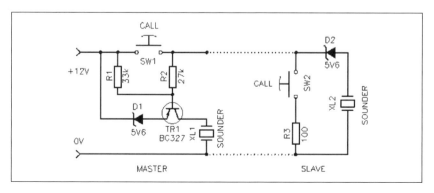

Fig 6.1. Intercom system

They are rated at 9V maximum and the zener diodes D1 and D2 serve to drop the 12V to around 7V. Zener diodes D1 and D2 are 500mW types and all resistors are 1/4W.

The 'Master' unit is housed in the shack and is powered from the 12V standby power supply so the system works even during a period of mains failure. When the 'Call' push button in the shack is pressed, SW1 sends 12V to the 'Slave' unit. This causes the sounder XL2 to squawk alerting the Domestic Executive (DE). Should the DE require the attention of the 'Master', by pressing SW2 a short is placed on the two wire lead connecting the two units and this causes TR1 to turn on and supply 12V to XL1 so making it squawk. The wire connecting the two units is normal figure-of-eight ripcord. The only important part is to get the interconnecting wire polarity correct, fitting polarised two-pin connectors at each end solves this. When neither call button is pressed the system draws zero current.

Although a very basic system it works surprisingly well with a 'code system' worked out by the Master and the DE. One squawk can mean the phone call is for you, two squawks might mean the dinner is ready etc.

'K' generator

I have included this circuit in this chapter as it may offend some purists! This item was popular some years ago and many amateurs were using one version or another. You either love this sort of thing or hate it; I will let you be the judge!

Basically, the infamous 'K' generator is an audio oscillator that sends the Morse character 'K' when the transmission ends. When the operator lets go of the PTT, the circuit holds the transmitter in transmit mode until the 'K' has been sent and then switches the transmitter off. I have seen many different circuits published over the years, some very basic and some very professional - even one using a PIC microprocessor, but that is taking things a bit far for those of us semi-literate in software code and programming. For what it's worth here is my circuit that uses low-cost discrete logic ICs and a few other common components.

The schematic is broken up into three drawings to get them on a page. It also makes the way the circuit works a bit easier to explain and understand. All resistors are 1/4W 5% and the diodes are all small signal silicon such as 1N914 or 1N4148. Electrolytic capacitors are solid tantalum, except C4, which is aluminium electrolytic. The NPN transistors can be your favorite types; BC107 and 2N2222 will also work.

Fig 6.2. 'K' generator timer circuit

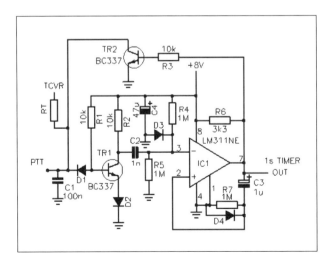

Fig 6.2 is the timer and PTT interface portion. The transmitter PTT line is connected to the microphone PTT switch and normally this is pulled up to some supply voltage on receive and pulled down to ground during transmit, at least that is the system used by about 99% of all transmitters I have seen. The resistor RT is the pull-up resistor in the transmitter; this will be supplied with a DC voltage between about 5V to 12V, depending on the transmitter.

When the PTT is held closed, the voltage on the base of TR1 is less than the forward bias to turn it on due to D2, and so the collector is pulled up to the supply rail by R1. (The 8V is arbitrary, if the transmitter has a supply available between 6V and 12V the circuit will work fine. I normally use 8V for circuits such as this. However, the supply rail chosen must be fairly stable. I normally steal a bit of power from the internal low voltage rail in the transmitter and this is often around 8 to 9V). When the PTT, is released the collector voltage of TR1 will drop to close to zero volts be-cause TR1 has turned on. The falling edge signal is connected to the volt-age comparator IC1 via a low value capacitor, C2. The falling edge causes the output of IC1 to toggle from the low state (zero volt condition) up to the supply rail because of the pull up resistor R6. The output will remain high until the RC timing capacitor C3 has discharged via R7. When this occurs, the output of IC1 will be pulled low to zero volts and stay there until it is triggered again. This is a monostable oscillator that only reacts to a falling edge. The time that the output is high is determined by the time constant of R7 and C3, with the values shown it is approx. 0.7s.

While the output of IC1 is high it also turns on TR2. TR2 holds the transmitter PTT on until the timer has timed out. The output of IC1 is also connected to the next portion of circuitry, the Morse code generator. This is covered in **Fig 6.3**.

The Morse code character 'K' is generated by IC2. This is a CD4017B, which is a decade counter. The clock for the counter is IC3A, 1/4 of a CD4093 NAND gate. IC3A generates a square wave signal that clocks IC2. C5 and R8 set the rate at which the character is clocked out. To vary the speed, make R8 a different value. Increasing R8 will slow the speed, but be aware that the whole character must be clocked out in less time than IC1 holds the input to IC3B high. With the values shown the clock runs at

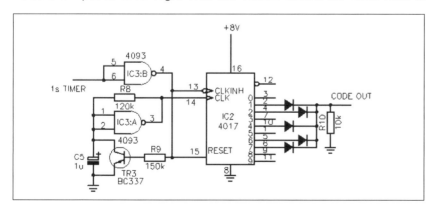

Fig 6.3. Morse code generator

approx 10Hz which is about 12WPM. If the frequency of IC3A is made too high the character clocked out will contain more than the correct number of clock periods. (If the clock were running 10 to 15% too fast the next character would be the Morse character 'C'). Hence the clock frequency should be such that the final output of IC2 (pin 11) is about to or has just gone high when the 1s timer terminates the sequence. This could have been solved by taking the output from pin 9 and using it via another monostable to force the counter to be reset, but his involves another IC which occupies more board space and so wasn't used.

The 'Clock Inhibit' and 'Reset' pins are driven by another portion of IC3, IC3B. The clock oscillator is also disabled by TR3, which pulls the input gates down to ground to stop the oscillator. The input to IC3B is the 1s timer signal from IC1 on the previous diagram. For the counter to advance, the Clock Inhibit pin and the Reset need to be low, which occurs when the 1s timer output is high. The CD4017 pulls each output high sequentially for a time period corresponding to one clock duration. When a particular output falls low the series diode prevents it affecting the other outputs.

The Morse character 'K' is a total of nine clock periods (draw it out on a piece of paper to convince yourself if you don't believe me!) A 'dash' is three time periods and a 'dot' is one time period. The inter- character spacing is equal to one dot. Hence, as the CD4017 has 10 outputs that go high sequentially we can code a character of up to nine time periods maximum by connecting diodes to a common point. This is known as 'diode OR - ing'. (Other characters that can be coded in nine time periods are A, B, D, E, F, H, I, L, N, S, W etc).

However, I found that when the correct 3:1 ratio was used, the character sounded very 'dull' and by reducing the dash length to two clock periods it sounds quite a bit better. This also solved another problem. When the clock starts pulsing the input the Reset pin forces the count to 0 and the first logical count output is 0 which causes the character to sounds uneven because the first Dash is noticeably longer than the second dash.

The summation point of the diodes forces the voltage across R10 high when a diode is connected and low when no diode is in circuit. When the 10th time period occurs, the 1s timer should time out and the circuit is inhibited by the Clock Inhibit and Reset pins being pulled high.

The final portion, shown in **Fig 6.4**, is the audio oscillator and audio filter. This connects to the Code Out point on Fig 6.3. This voltage is a DC representation of the character 'K' in Morse code. IC3C is an inverter that drives TR4 and grounds the audio oscillator input when its input is low. When the Code Out signal is high the transistor TR4 is off and the oscillator runs normally.

Fig 6.4. Audio oscillator and filter

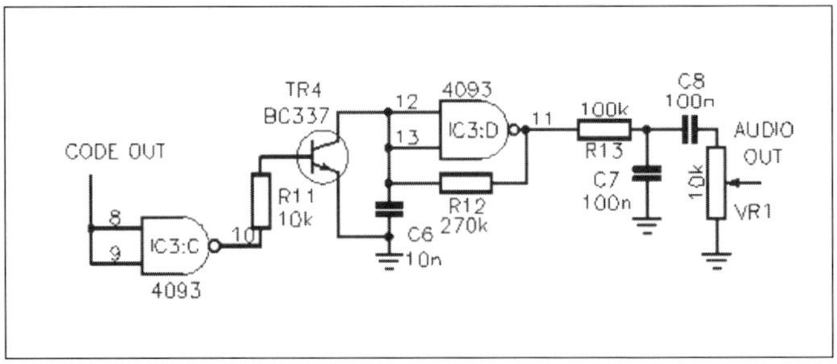

The oscillator (IC3D) runs and generates a keyed audio square wave signal of about 1kHz. Because a square wave is a bit harsh, the brute force RC filter of R13 and C7 knocks off the sharp edges. This leaves a fairly clean signal to send to the transmitter microphone amplifier stages. Although the output signal is more like a triangle waveform this shouldn't be a big issue as the transmission time is very short and the transmitter microphone amplifier stages should have audio processing to remove high frequency components. VR1 sets the output level. The signal is routed to the microphone input of the transmitter.

Poor man's Christmas tree light flasher

Christmas tree lights are normally a string of 20 12V lamps all connected in series across the 230V AC mains supply. Special lamps can be bought that contain a bi-metallic strip that heats up due to the lamp filament and then interrupts the supply. When the bi-metallic strip cools down the circuit is made again and the lights are lit again. The time constant is a bit variable and the special lamps are quite expensive. Here is a cheap way of flashing a string of low voltage lamps that needs no expensive flasher lamp.

The flasher is a readily available fluorescent lamp starter. This circuit can handle lamps up to about 40W.

The fluorescent starter Q1 is connected in series with the string of 20 x 12V lamps or 40 x 6V lamps. At switch on the current flowing causes ionisation in the neon glow tube. The ionisation in the neon glow tube starter generates heat. This heat is transferred to the internal bi-metallic strip and then the switch closes supplying the full 230V to the string of lamps. The bi-metallic strip in Q1 when closed shorts out the neon lamp which stops glowing and the bi-metallic switch cools and the switch then opens.

The advantage of this circuit to the normal type is that there is a small pre-heating current flowing in the lamps when the switch is open. This raises the temperature of the lamp filaments, although not enough to cause them to glow noticeably, it is a type of 'black heat', so reducing the inrush current when the switch closes to supply full 230V to the string of lamps. This increases the life of the lamps considerably. The starter also contains radio interference suppression so the switching does not affect medium-wave radios with switching clicks.

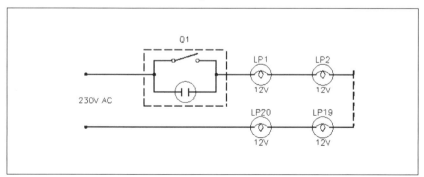

Fig 6.5. Cheap Christmas tree light flasher

Wind speed indicator

Many radio amateurs have an interest in the prevailing weather conditions. For VHF operators they can give a warning of enhanced propagation. All amateurs need some warning if the wind exceeds the safe limits of the antenna system. Although one can buy a complete weather station, they are quite expensive. The design in **Fig 6.6** is for the wind speed indicator. The temperature-measuring portion could use a precision temperature IC such as the LM35 described earlier.

There are many ways to measure wind speed; the commonest version is a device known as a 'cup-anemometer'. This normally consists of three half-spherical cups fixed to a delta shaped frame that drives a pulse generator or DC generator. Either type will work but will require calibrating. The simplest method of calibrating is to mount the cup anemometer on the roof rack of a car and drive at different speeds, noting the results, and then mark the scale of the indicator accordingly. The cups can be made by slicing ping pong balls in half with a sharp hobby knife and gluing them to stiff rods made from brass brazing rod using two-part epoxy adhesive. The three brass rods are soldered together to make the delta shape and an adapter made to fit the motor shaft tightly. After assembly, paint the cups with polyurethane varnish to waterproof them.

Fig 6.6. Wind speed indicator

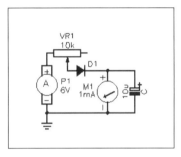

The DC generator P1 is a small permanent magnet motor as used in small toys. The cup-anemometer is fixed to the shaft and the motor mounted in a waterproof enclosure. The wind causes the motor shaft to rotate. The higher the wind speed the faster the motor will rotate and the greater the output voltage developed will be. Preset VR1 serves to calibrate the meter against wind speed. The cup-anemometer should be mounted near the top of the tower or mast on a cross arm so you get a true indication of the prevailing wind.

CHAPTER 7

Some antenna items

In this chapter:

- Constructing Yagi antennas
- Heavy-duty elevator
- Control circuits

M UCH OF this chapter is devoted to solving the problems associated with making a heavy-duty elevator system for use on a large EME array. We start, though, with a look at making Yagi booms, and connecting the elements to the boom.

Constructing Yagi antennas

When constructing a typical Yagi we need to attach the various elements to the boom. Very often with a bit of ingenuity we can utilise off the shelf hardware to make life easier. The boom is normally selected to be a length of aluminium tubing and these typically are available in lengths of 3.1m, 5m and 6.2m for diameters from 25mm to 51mm. For low-band Yagis the boom will end up being quite long and two lengths of tubing may need to be joined to make the boom long enough. Making a joint between two similar size pieces of tubing can be tricky and if it fails considerable damage can be

Fig 7.1. Element to boom attachment method

caused, not only to the antenna but also to surrounding objects! A popular method is to use a piece of tubing with an internal diameter the same as the two tubes and then to drill several holes and pass bolts through the section to form a secure joint.

Where the frequency is higher we can often get by with standard length tubing. Attaching the elements can be difficult but the method I have adopted gives good results and sufficient strength to sustain quite high winds. Living on a mountaintop means we have hurricanes of up to 160KPH at some times of the year, so my antennas need to be engineered to a higher standard than most.

A typical element mounting is shown in **Fig 7.1**. This is for a 50MHz Yagi and uses 13mm diameter tubing. The boom to element clamp is a standard television antenna item. The one-piece element passes through a thick wall aluminium tube and the U-bolts pass through this. The element is

Fig 7.2. Driven element mounting hardware

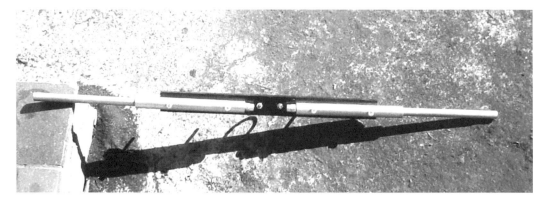

held in place in the outer sleeve by either self-tapping screws or pop-rivets. **Fig 7.3. Close up of driven element centre** The outer tube is 4mm-wall thickness with an internal diameter of approx 14mm and is very substantial. This is a standard item from stockists of aluminium in this country (South Africa).

The driven element normally needs to be split in the centre and insulated from the boom, so a different method is used. The driven element is made in two pieces per element. The centre portion is made from 15mm OD tube into which a 13mm tube is a push fit. The main strength comes from the 4mm wall thickness outer tube, this measures 21mm OD and has an internal diameter of 14mm, so the pieces need to be drilled out slightly to suit the 15mm OD element inner pieces. The outer pieces can be slid in and out in the 15mm tube to set the resonant length. The 15mm tube has several saw cuts so it can be closed tightly on to the 13mm tube. This is provided by stainless steel hose clamps (Jubilee clips). The elements are supported on a length of thick paxolin (Tufnol) with 6mm bolts. The inner ends of the element have an aluminium plug pressed in and fixed by an M4 or 4BA screw. The end of the slug is also drilled and tapped to take another M4 or 4BA screw. The two screws are for attaching the feed points. Where a hairpin loop is required, the top screws are used and the balun connects to the end holes with solder tags.

The paxolin strip is 12mm thick and wide enough to support the element. A U-bolt attaches the paxolin strip to the boom. The paxolin strip is heavily coated with polyurethane yacht varnish to protect it from the weather. The advantage of this method is that by slackening the U-bolt nuts and sliding the element along the boom to a new position we can easily change the element spacings.

Heavy duty elevator

For large EME ('moonbounce') arrays the average commercial elevators are simply not strong enough. When I was assembling a 2m EME station a home-brewed elevator was made. This is capable of supporting the largest array likely to be used.

The basis is a hinged arrangement with one portion bolted to the rotatable mast and the main cross boom for the array bolted to the movable portion. A worm drive gearbox was found in a local scrap yard with a 40:1 reduction. A large 24V windscreen wiper motor from a commercial vehicle drives the gearbox. The gearbox has a winch drum attached to the output shaft and 4mm diameter galvanised iron wire stranded rope is attached to a shackle of the fixed part.

When the motor is driven in one direction the rope is paid out and the movable portion falls under the weight of the array. When the motor is driven in the opposite direction the rope is wound on to the winch drum and this pulls the two portions back together. A limit switch is fitted for the fully closed position, which trips the relay for the downward drive. Hence, you can switch to downwards drive and walk away to do other things. The rate of travel is quite slow, about 30s between zero elevation and 90°.

Some pictures of the elevator are shown here after it was removed for servicing, having been in use for five years. It is quite dirty and the motor was suffering from water ingress.

Fig 7.4. View of worm gearbox and winch drum drive. The over limit micro-switch is above the gearbox and connects with the vertical member when fully closed. The main array cross boom is fastened with two U-bolts to the movable portion. Substantial clamps welded to the framework bolt the fixed portion to the rotating mast

When first constructed the elevator was tested by loading it with buckets of water. It can easily lift 200kg. The wire rope is rated at 350kg safe load and a breaking load of almost one ton. The framework and components weigh approx 30kg.

The elevator framework is made from 50mm x 6mm angle iron with bracing straps welded in position to prevent the framework from twisting under the heavy loads. The main array cross boom is a 50mm diameter thick wall aluminium tube (5mm wall), internally braced with ribs, and approx 8m in length. (This was a specially sourced piece of tubing made for yacht masts). From the ends of the cross boom two 6m long 50mm tubes support the Yagis on each end. Hence, the Yagis were supported in an 8m x 6m box configuration and horizontally polarised.

Alternative sources of motors are the types used for gate motors that are fitted with a suitable reduction gearbox and have a gear to engage in a rack to move the gate sideways. These are normally 12V DC motors but adequately powerful if used for intermittent operation. It is important the gearbox is a worm drive type as this prevents the shaft from rotating under load and provides braking when the motor coasts down to a stop.

Another important consideration is the attachment of the shackle to the end of the winch rope. This should be a heavy-duty swaged crimp type and the rope must pass around a thimble to prevent chafing. The thimble connects to a shackle allowing some flexibility and self-alignment as the angle of the winch rope varies throughout the full travel.

The motor control relays are contained in the waterproof box at the bottom. The box also contains an elevation indication potentiometer with a weighted pendulum. Not shown are the safety ropes in case the main wire rope breaks. These prevent

Fig 7.5. Attachment to the rotatable mast is by the heavy-duty clamps. The hinge pin is a 16mm diameter silver steel round bar running in bronze bushes. The total height is approx 400mm

Fig 7.6. General view of the elevator

107

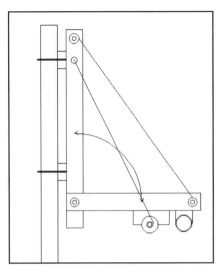

Fig 7.7. General arrangement of elevator - side view. Shown in maximum elevation position

the array going beyond about 100° elevation. The two safety ropes attach between the fixed portion and the movable portion to prevent the elevation exceeding approx 100°. These need to be much higher breaking strength than the winch cable, because if the winch cable breaks the array will fall suddenly and will have considerable kinetic energy. In my case some vehicle winch cable was obtained and heavy buckle clamps attach these to the framework. These cables are rated at five tons safe load but are quite thick, approx 8mm diameter.

Control circuits

The shack end of the elevator system has a small box that contains the power supply, indicator meter and the control switches. The elevator box contains relays and interlocking switches. The current drawn by the DC motor is quite high: for a large 12V windscreen wiper motor the current is approx 8A. This would cause excessive volts drop in the wiring between the shack and the elevator if the length of wiring were more than a few metres. In my case the control cable was approx 20m long and so the cable would need to be a substantial gauge for the two motor wires.

Because the DC motor needs to be reversible, it is necessary for there to be two relays, each rated at the required current. Automotive double-pole relays were used with 12V coils. A lead-acid sealed battery of 14AH was positioned close to the elevator on the tower fitted in a weatherproof box to supply the high current to drive the motor. This battery is trickle charged by a 12V regulator in the control box in the shack. A 30VA mains transformer and bridge rectifier provide the main power supply. This is shown in **Fig 7.8**. Although I originally used a 24V DC motor, more affordable 12V motors are now available and so the circuits show 12V operation. The gate

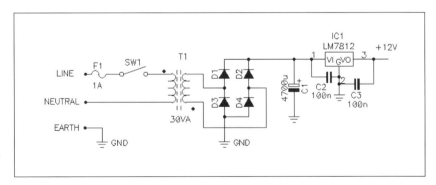

Fig 7.8. Elevator power supply

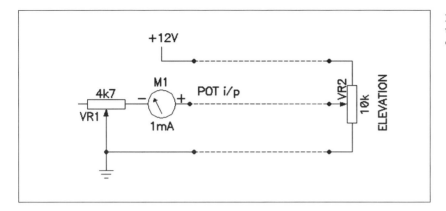

Fig 7.9. Elevation indication circuit

drive motors normally have a 100:1 reduction gearbox and are adequately rated with the second gearbox in series.

Diodes D1 to D4 can be 3A diodes or a packaged bridge rated at 3A. The transformer secondary can be about 12 to 15V AC. The indicator is fed with a three-core lead with the stabilised 12V supply and the pendulum weight arranged so that the potentiometer is at the zero travel when the antenna is at zero elevation. As the antenna is elevated the pendulum weight causes the potentiometer shaft to rotate. The potentiometer has 270° of rotation. The maximum output voltage is one-third of the supply when at 90° elevation, approx 4.5V maximum when at 100° elevation and a 12V supply. I found a square panel meter with 90° travel and this was scaled 0 to 100. Hence, the maximum elevation indicated is 100°, which is 10° over travel. This meter was 1mA FSD and so a scaling resistor was used to set the indication by adjusting the sensitivity preset. The switches to control the direction of travel can be simple toggle switches or a three position single pole rotary switch with the centre position unused. In the diagram are shown two toggle switches; one is a single-pole double throw and the second is a single-pole make type. The 12V from the supply is carried up the main control cable to the elevator and this switches the coils of the relays to drive the DC motor in the required direction.

Note that the ground end of the indicator potentiometer has a dedicated ground return in the main control cable. This is to prevent false meter readings when the motor is active. In total two ground wires are needed, the second serves the battery negative and relay grounding.

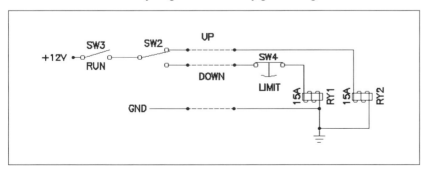

Fig 7.10. Motor drive control circuits

Fig 7.11. Motor drive switching and charging circuits

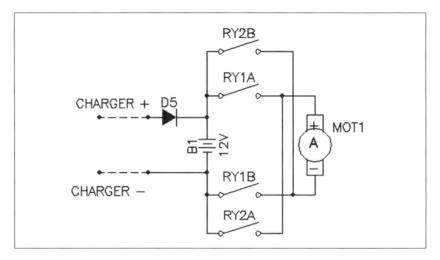

The motor control relays are wired to reverse the motor direction by selecting the appropriate polarity of the battery supply. The 12V lead-acid battery is trickle charged by the 12V supply fed up the control cable from the control box in the shack. The limit switch SW4 in the 'Down' control relay ensures the elevator is not over driven when reeling in the winch rope on the gearbox pulley. Without this the danger exists that it can be pulled too tight and the rope could snap. This micro-switch is a waterproof type because it is exposed to the weather. These are commonly used on machine tools tables to limit the traverse. Another limit switch could also be fitted in the 'Up' control line although the safety ropes prevent any over travel and the mounting of a suitable micro-switch is not as simple, however, it could be contrived if felt necessary.

Diode D5 can be a 3A silicon type 1N5400. It prevents the battery discharging when the system is powered down. The control cable can be quite a small gauge of wire as no current greater than 1A is required, that being the maximum charging current to the battery. I used commonly available eight-core light duty rotator cable, with one spare wire as only seven cores are required. If a large gauge wire is used it may be necessary to include a low value resistor (approx 5Ω) in series with the positive charging lead to limit the current drawn when the motor is running to prevent the metering being upset. An alternative method is to use a lower voltage for the indicator potentiometer derived from a low power zener diode and dropper resistor from the unregulated supply. The scaling resistor and potentiometer value will need adjusting to suit the meter used and the supply voltage chosen.

Fig 7.12. Elevator control unit. The elevation control uses a three-position rotary switch

CHAPTER 8

Radio Frequency circuits

In this chapter:

- Constant amplitude crystal oscillator
- Infinite impedance detector
- Overtone crystal oscillator
- High power PIN diode antenna switch
- PIN diode variable attenuator
- Low distortion transmit mixer
- Phase modulator for an FM transmitter
- Multi-channel crystal oscillator
- Simple high gain IF amplifier
- Product detector for SSB or CW reception
- A high performance log-amplifier
- A lower cost approach

MANY ITEMS the amateur constructor builds use what design engineers call 'building blocks'. To save re-inventing the wheel every time a new design is performed most designers have a stock of favourite circuits they use over and over again as they have been proven in previous designs.

Constant amplitude crystal oscillator

When a constant amplitude crystal oscillator is required the circuit shown in **Fig 8.1** is a good choice. When several crystals are switched using a common oscillator, for example a 2m transmitter oscillator chain, the different activity of the crystals causes the output level to vary. If the crystal oscillator is feeding a reactance modulator to generate modulation for a FM transmitter the deviation for each channel may be different. This circuit uses RF feedback to a signal diode to provide AGC action that maintains constant output amplitude.

The oscillator is a Pierce circuit for a fundamental crystal. The feedback for the AGC is by C1 and this develops a negative voltage across gate 1 of the Dual Gate mosfet. If the output amplitude increases the negative

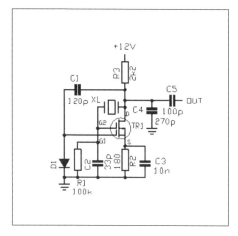

Fig 8.1. Crystal
oscillator with
AGC

bias on gate 1 also increases so reducing the gain, this maintains constant output amplitude. D1 is a small signal silicon diode such as a 1N914 or 1N4148. TR1 can be any VHF Dual Gate mosfet, such as a BF982, BF961 or BF989.

The component values shown suit a crystal frequency of 8 to 12MHz. The output amplitude is quite low, typically 200mV p-p across a 1kΩ load with a 12V supply. Like all oscillators it requires buffering by a high impedance amplifier to reduce any pulling by the following stages. The output coupling capacitor C5 should be a small value and only large enough to deliver adequate drive to the following buffer amplifier. This gives the best frequency stability.

Infinite impedance detector

When a very linear AM detector is required the best circuit is the 'infinite impedance detector'. Originally developed for valve broadcast receivers we can today use a solid state version with a junction field effect transistor. The infinite Z detector has very low harmonic distortion and as the name suggests appears as practically infinite impedance to the stage driving it.

The input to the detector is taken from the last IF amplifier stage collector tuned circuit. Coupling into TR1 is via a small capacitor C1. The gate resistor can be very high in value so the loading on the final IF amplifier stage is basically the gate capacitance of TR1 shunted by R1. A typical JFET gate capacity is approx 2pF so the loading is practically zero. For best performance the input signal needs to be at least 2V p-p, which with a high Q IF tuned circuit is very easy to achieve. The detected audio signal is developed across the source resistor R3 and the IF signal is low pass filtered by R4 and C3. The audio signal is coupled out via C4. This should be fed to a high impedance audio amplifier stage.

Fig 8.2. Infinite
impedance de-
tector for AM

The supply voltage should be between 6 and 10V for best performance. Typical audio distortion figures with 2V p-p input at 60% AM with 1kHz modulation is of the order of 0.1%. At 10kHz modulating audio the distortion is approx 0.5%. These figures are far superior to most AM detectors found in amateur receivers, which mostly use detector diodes, because AM is something of an afterthought for most commercially-manufactured amateur receivers.

An AGC voltage can be taken from the junction of R4 and C3 suitably filtered and used to control the IF stages gain. The DC voltage increases as the input signal increases.

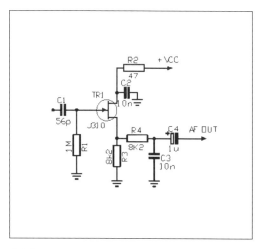

Overtone crystal oscillator

Here is a circuit for an overtone crystal oscillator suitable for third and fifth order crystals. This would suit crystals from about 25MHz to 120MHz and is suitable for many items of VHF and UHF equipment.

The circuit is shown in **Fig 8.3**. The transistors used need to have good high frequency performance; BFW92A or BFR92 (SMD) and MPSH-10 are good choices. The inductor L1 in series with the crystal needs to be correctly dimensioned to suit the operating frequency. The series tuned network C1 and L1 should be series resonant at the crystal frequency. A ferrite slug tuned coil in a screening can is the best option. The resistor across the crystal suppresses the crystal fundamental mode (parallel resonance). This resistor should have a value of not less than approx 10 times the ESR of the crystal. 680Ω is often the optimum value. Too low a value will reduce the amplitude and too high a value will cause spurious resonance modes.

Feedback is derived from the capacitive potential divider between the base and emitter of the oscillator transistor. The base is biased to half the supply rail by the high value resistors. The oscillator feeds an emitter follower with a low value of coupling capacitor. The oscillator needs a well-stabilised supply for best frequency stability.

To set up the oscillator, remove the crystal and fit a resistor of 10 to 39Ω in place of it. Adjust L1 to bring the oscillator on to frequency. Remove the resistor and refit the crystal and then adjust L1 to trim the crystal on to the exact frequency. It should be possible to pull the crystal frequency both higher and lower than its nominal frequency by a small amount. Having set the crystal on frequency, check that the oscillator starts up when the supply is turned off and on again. If the oscillator is reluctant to start, increase the value of the emitter resistor by 25% and try again. With a crystal with average activity the oscillator should start instantly.

Here is a guide to the value of L1 required for different frequencies using 15pF series capacitor:

```
25MHz = 2µH ± 15%
75MHz = 0.4µH ± 15%
120MHz = 0.1µH ± 10%
```

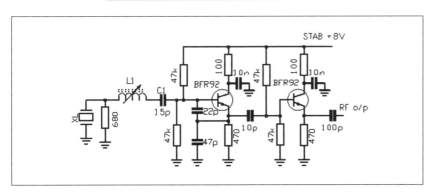

Fig 8.3. Overtone crystal oscillator

As the frequency increases C1 can be reduced in value from the 15pF shown; at 120MHz a good choice would be approx 5.6pF with an inductance of 0.5μH with a tuning range of ± 10%.

High power PIN diode antenna switch

When very fast switching of a transmitter and receiver are required on the VHF or UHF bands a PIN diode antenna changeover switch (T/R switch) is the answer. For packet radio and other data transmission modes, such as high speed Meteor Scatter, the slow operation of conventional relays reduces the throughput speed considerably. A typical antenna changeover relay requires about 50ms to switch reliably, a PIN diode switch can switch in about 5μs, an improvement of 10,000 times. Relays also have a limited life, 100,000 cycles being a typical specification.

However, PIN diode switching of high RF power does have a few problems. If the receiver is connected to the transmitter via a PIN diode that is biased off, the capacity of an off state PIN diode can be as high as 5pF. At VHF and UHF this is a fair bit of power being dumped into the receiver front end and may be enough to cause damage. To resolve this problem we can use the characteristic of a quarter-wave transmission line. This circuit is from an application note by Unitrode Corporation, manufacturers of PIN diodes. The company name changed to Microsemi Corporation some years ago. It offers a bandwidth of approx 20%, which would suit any of the amateur VHF or UHF bands.

If the circuit in **Fig 8.4** is examined, the PIN diode switch consists of two diodes. Capacitors C1, C2, C3 and C4 are DC blocking or coupling capacitors and have a very low reactance to the RF. D1 is in series with the transmitter port and D2 is effectively across the receiver input. When D1 is turned on, by connecting a positive supply to R1, D1 conducts and presents a low insertion loss to the RF signal from the transmitter to the antenna. With a good PIN diode we can expect as little as 0.1dB of loss. The current flows to ground in D2 and this is also turned hard on. This places a short across the receiver input and clamps the level of RF to a low level. Connecting D1 and D2 is a quarter-wave transmission line. When D2 is providing a short across the receiver input, the impedance at the other end of the line is an open circuit, so very little power tries to travel through the quarter-wave line.

Fig 8.4. PIN Diode T/R switch with quarter-wave line

The higher the DC bias-current the lower the insertion loss of the diodes. For a 1kW switch the current required is at least 500mA. Diodes can be the popular UM9401 for power levels up to 400W into a perfectly matched antenna (VSWR = 1:1) and 100W into an infinite VSWR antenna. This is with a forward diode current of 100mA. For higher RF power a higher power diode is required. The UM7000 diode will easily handle 5kW into a 1:1 VSWR

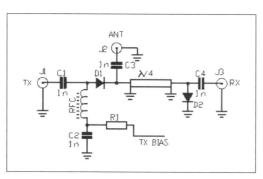

and about 1500W into an infinite VSWR load. This diode requires about 1A bias for lowest insertion loss. Running the calculations on the UM7000 series shows that it can handle peak pulse powers of over 60kW in short pulse radar applications with a 1% transmit duty cycle.

On receive the PIN diodes are both biased off. The load presented to the signal from the antenna by the transmitter is very small, the PIN diode in the *off-state* looks like a high value resistor of greater than 10kΩ shunted by the junction capacitance of about 2 to 5pF. The signal from the antenna passes through the low-loss quarter-wave line to the receiver input with virtually zero insertion loss. With careful construction and good PIN diodes this changeover switch can handle powers in excess of 1kW with receiver isolation as high as 70dB.

The switching time is almost entirely dependant on how quickly the PIN diode bias current can be switched on and off, this normally being the limiting factor and not the switching time of the PIN diodes which switch in about 1µs or less. The drive circuit must be able to charge and discharge any decoupling or coupling capacitors rapidly, this requires a driver that can source and sink several Amperes of current for the time period to charge and discharge the capacitors. The best choice is the 'totem-pole' configuration (see **Fig 8.5**). The value of the dropper resistor needs to be calculated with the supply voltage to achieve the correct bias current. Often a driver similar to that used for switch-mode mosfets gate drive can be modified to give the required switching speed. If you analyse Fig 8.4, there is a total of 4nF of capacity effectively in parallel with the switching voltage and this needs to be charged and discharged each time the switch toggles from receive to transmit or back again.

When the Tx / Rx signal is high, TR1 is turned on. TR2 is hence turned on, supplying bias current to the PIN diodes via the current limiting resistor R4. When the Tx / Rx signal goes low, TR1 and TR2 turn off and TR3 is turned hard on, so discharging the decoupling capacitors via R4. This ensures a rapid switching of the PIN diodes.

For low VHF bands the length of the quarter-wave coaxial line becomes quite long. If RG58/U is used for the transmission line for a 50MHz T/R switch this requires a length of approx 1m of cable. We can use an alternative

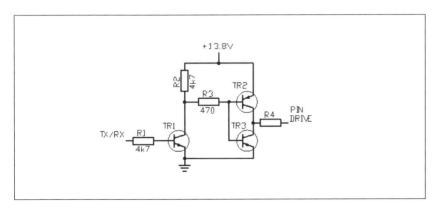

Fig 8.5. 'Totem pole' driver

115

Fig 8.6. PIN diode changeover switch with lumped line

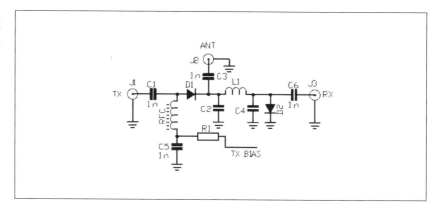

circuit that simulates a quarter-wave transmission line with an inductor and two capacitors. This is shown in **Fig 8.6**.

This circuit works in exactly the same way as Fig 8.4, except that the quarter-wave line is replaced with L1, C2 and C4. The formula to calculate the values of L1, C2 and C4 is:

$$L1 = \frac{Zo}{2 \pi F} \text{ and } C2, C4 = \frac{1}{2 \pi F \, Zo}$$

where Zo is the system impedance and F is the operating frequency.

For 50MHz the values are L = 159nH, C2, C4 = 63.6pF in a 50Ω system.

The inductor L1 can be made very compact if wound on a ferrite toroidal core and so the switch becomes small. The layout and grounding is critical to get the best isolation and lowest insertion loss on transmit and receive. Screening will probably be needed between the various sections to prevent RF signals from bypassing the quarter-wave lumped section.

The inductor RFC used to feed the bias current into the network must be rated to handle the DC bias current and also be capable of withstanding the RF p-p voltage developed by the transmitter. The self-resonant frequency of the RFC must be well above the operating frequency; the shunting capacitance of the coupling capacitors lowers the SRF considerably. The reactance of RFC should at least 10 times that of the system impedance at the operating frequency.

To give some indication of what can be achieved with the right components and a good circuit layout, in the 1980s I built a switch like the one detailed for a 1kW VHF frequency hopping jammer. The transmit / receive times were less than 12.5µs, being solely the limitations of the diode driver. This design used 2A forward bias on the diodes and the measured insertion loss on transmit was 0.06dB at the 1kW level. Receive insertion loss was slightly higher at 0.09dB at 80MHz and transmitter to receiver isolation was approx 75dB mid-band.

To increase the transmitter to receiver isolation even more, a low power PIN diode can be connected across the receiver input and driven from the same control signal as the main diodes. This will increase the isolation by about 20 to 30dB. Lower power versions of this circuit using a double pole LC network (two in series) with two shunt diodes on the receive port exceeded 120dB isolation when correctly built.

PIN diode variable attenuator

A variable attenuator is required for many applications. This circuit uses low power PIN diodes to vary the attenuation over a wide bandwidth using a DC control voltage. The minimum insertion loss is about 2dB and the maximum as high as 40dB. The RF portion is shown in **Fig 8.7**.

The attenuator suits a 50Ω system impedance. The diodes are connected in a Bridged Tee configuration. The circuit in **Fig 8.8** performs the control of the diode currents.

Suitable diodes for the attenuator are the BA479 series by Vishay Semiconductors. The diodes used for D1 and D2 do not have to be PIN diodes. Many AC rectifier diodes such as the 1N4000 series or small signal diodes such as the 1N914 will work in this circuit at low power up to about 100MHz.

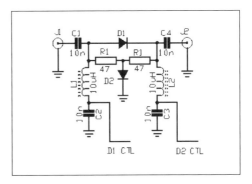

Fig 8.7. Continuously variable attenuator

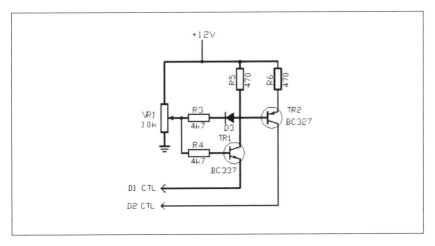

Fig 8.8. PIN attenuator control circuit

Low distortion transmit mixer

When a mixer is required to convert a low frequency RF signal to a higher one, for example a transverter for 6m driven by a 28MHz SSB transceiver, a balanced mixer with good linearity is required. Some devices we could use are double-balanced diode ring mixers, balanced FET mixers, twin tetrode valves or bipolar transistors. Most amateurs regard the last one as a poor choice. However, using bipolar transistors in a push-pull mixer can give very good results as I discovered when designing a 6m transverter.

This mixer used a RCA IC, the CA3028. Sadly this device disappeared off the market some time ago so I was very surprised to find it recently reintroduced, albeit only in a surface mount version. RCA went through some name changes along the way, becoming Harris and today it is Intersil that manufactures it. The CA3028 is supplied in an 8-pin SO8 package. National Semiconductor also manufactured a version under the part number LM3028.

Mixing from 28MHz to 50MHz means we only have one choice of the LO signal (this being 22MHz) because we wish to avoid inverting the sidebands. If we only have a 28MHz transmitter with USB we are stuck with this arrangement. A problem with using 28 + 22MHz is that the spurious products fall close to the wanted output frequency. 2 x 22MHz = 44MHz and 2 x 28MHz = 56MHz which makes filtering the output of the mixer a bit more difficult.

A better choice would be 14MHz as the drive signal with a 36MHz LO. This still maintains the sideband sense. An even better plan would be to use an even lower HF band such as 10MHz and an LO of 40MHz or the alternative LO of 60MHz, but this inverts the sidebands and so the driver needs to be set to LSB to obtain USB at 50MHz.

Providing the drive signal isn't too high, the CA3028 mixer to be described will give excellent linearity. The intermodulation performance is normally degraded far more by the RF power amplifier stages following the mixer. As a good rule of thumb, the IMD performance of stages moving back from the PA need to be approx 6dB better per stage. So if we require a final IMD of -30dBc the driver stage needs to give an IMD figure of -36dBc, the preceding stage -42dBc etc. If we have, say, four stages from the mixer to the PA, the IMD of the mixer needs to be 24dB better than the final IMD figure. This means that the up-mixer needs to deliver an IMD figure of -54dBc if the final IMD is -30dBc.

The internal diagram of the CA3028 is shown in **Fig 8.9**. The IC consists of three closely matched NPN RF transistors made on one substrate. The high frequency performance is guaranteed to at least 100MHz and the matching between the individual transistors is excellent with temperature variation.

The configuration is known as a 'Gilbert Cell' and the bottom transistor controls the collector currents of the two top transistors. The circuit can be connected in many different ways. Pin 3 is normally the ground although it does not have to be. For use as a mixer the LO is connected to either pin 2 or pin 4 via a capacitor and the input signal to pins 1 and 5 in a *push-pull* drive. The resulting mixing product is available at the two collectors, pins 6 and 8, and is also push-pull. The LO drive is effectively in *push-push*

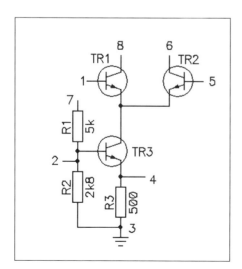

Fig 8.9. CA3028 internal diagram

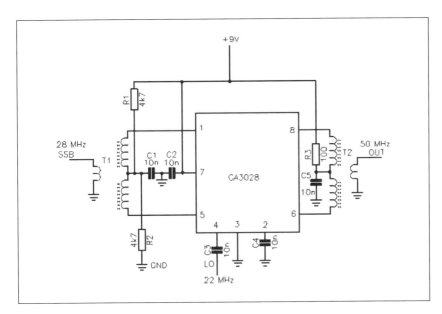

Fig   8.10.
CA3028 SSB up-
mixer

and cancels out at the collectors of TR1 and TR2 because of the inherent well matched characteristics of TR1 and TR2.

Pin 4 can be decoupled with a capacitor if pin 2 is used as the LO input to increase the gain, or left floating where less gain is satisfactory. TR3 can be used as grounded base or grounded emitter because the pins are not committed. The push-pull transformer for the driving signal is connected across the bases of TR1 and TR2 and needs to have a very low DC resistance to ensure the balance is not upset. The base bias for the top transistors is normally fed in at the centre tap of the transformer. Similarly the output at the collectors uses another push-pull transformer and the collector supply is fed into the centre tap. Link coupling windings allow the input and output transformers to be connected to the rest of the circuit and the impedance ratio can be varied by using transmission-line transformers wound on ferrite cores (*Ruthroff transformers*).

The power gain when operated as a linear mixer is quite low, typically about 6dB for best linearity. Similarly for best intermodulation performance the input drive level should be low, about 5mW maximum although 1mW would be better. Hence, the mixer should provide an output level of about 4mW with 1mW of input signal. This is then filtered with a band-pass filter to remove spurious mixing products (see Chapter 7 for a suitable design).

The LO input is injected on to the emitter resistor of TR3 and TR3 base is decoupled so it operates as a grounded base transistor. The impedance looking into pin 4 is close to 50Ω and with this configuration the LO power required is about 10mW. If the LO is injected into pin 2 the impedance is about 1kΩ and the decoupling capacitor should be moved to pin 4. In this configuration the LO power required is less but it needs to develop about 1V p-p across pin 2 for best efficiency.

The transformers used for the input and output can be wound on ferrite toroid cores with tri-filar wire. A swamping resistor can be fitted across T1 if the SSB drive is excessive. The maximum supply voltage is 12V but for most applications the use of 9V is to be preferred.

The LO suppression with no SSB drive should be of the order of 40dB, this is very dependant on the balance obtained in T2. The measured IMD performance with 1mW SSB input and 10mW of LO was -50dBc for third order products and -60dBc for fifth order products. As with most mixers the IMD performance is very dependant on the drive levels, for best IMD the LO level should be 10dB higher than the SSB drive signal, up to a maximum of about 20mW LO drive (+13dBm in 50Ω). Increasing the LO drive above this causes the gain to fall as the transistors are driven into saturation.

This push-pull mixer also makes an excellent receive mixer for an HF receiver where the first IF is higher than the input signal.

Phase modulator for an FM transmitter

One of the best methods of generating a very linear frequency modulated signal is a phase modulator. The other method is to use a varicap diode to pull a crystal to generate FM directly. This often results in asymmetrical modulation and consequent distortion because a crystal cannot normally be pulled equal amounts about the centre frequency. A phase modulator gives very symmetrical modulation and hence very low distortion. The phase modulator is often called an 'indirect FM' modulator, whereas the pulled crystal type is known as 'direct FM'. The circuit to be shown is one a colleague and I designed for a VHF two-way radio transmitter for mid-band and high-band applications. This gives a distortion figure of less than 1% at the normal 2/3rd peak deviation with a 1kHz audio tone (3kHz deviation for a 25kHz channel spaced transmitter using 5kHz peak deviation).

The circuits that follow are a phase modulator, a multi-channel crystal oscillator and a switching circuit that allows the individual channels to

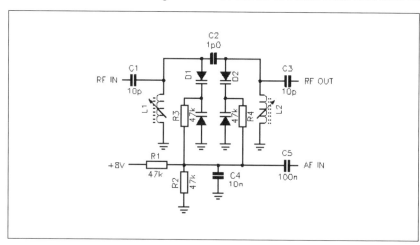

Fig 8.11. Phase modulator circuit

be adjusted for the lowest distortion. (The phase modulator is shown configured for a single channel application. See the notes later when multi-channel operation is required).

The basic phase modulator shown in **Fig 8.11** is a double-tuned band-pass filter with a very small value top coupling capacitor to give a critically coupled response centred on the crystal oscillator frequency. The component values shown suit a centre frequency of about 6 to 8MHz. The band-pass centre frequency is moved by the variable capacitance diodes D1 and D2. These are dual-diodes in a common package although four well-matched single diodes can also be used. In this case each diode needs to be twice the value of a dual diode. I used a Toko Semiconductors dual diode with a total capacitance of 50pF with 4V bias. Alternatives would be the BB204 or BB304 by Vishay Semiconductors. Inductors L1 and L2 are high Q adjustable screened coils of a value to resonate with the value of D1 and D2. At 7MHz the values of L1 and L2 are approx 8.5µH.

The output of the crystal oscillator and buffer amplifier at low impedance is applied at the RF IN port. R1 and R2 set the DC bias on the varicap diodes to half rail. This moves the diodes into a very linear portion of the capacitance versus voltage curve. With no modulation applied the inductors L1 and L2 are adjusted for maximum output voltage at the RF Out port. This sets the band-pass filter to a critically coupled response. The stage following the modulator needs to be a high impedance to prevent loading on the modulator. The audio input level is approx 200mV rms for maximum deviation.

When audio is applied to the varicap diodes the band-pass filter centre frequency is swung above and below the nominal centre frequency, producing an output signal similar to a partially modulated AM signal if viewed on an oscilloscope. The subsequent amplitude variations are removed in the following hard limiting multiplier stages so completing the amplitude to phase conversion (AM to PM conversion). However, the phase shift is limited to approx ±45° for the lowest distortion. Hence, the phase modulation needs to be performed at a low frequency and the multiplier stages need to be at least eight times for best distortion. For a total deviation of 5kHz at 50MHz the multiplier stages need to be eight times minimum.

Phase modulators inherently have a rising response to the audio signal of 6dB / octave, so the audio applied needs to be correctly shaped to maintain a flat audio frequency response. This means that the microphone amplifier stage feeding the modulator needs to have a -6dB / octave response to about 2.5kHz and then a very sharp cut off to prevent over deviation for the higher audio frequencies. If a constant amplitude audio signal of 1kHz is applied and the deviation set by a preset control, the deviation will double if a 2kHz tone is then applied. This is known as 'pre-emphasis' and is

The way the phase modulator works is exactly the same as using an AM receiver to 'slope detect' an FM signal. In a slope detector the IF is slightly off-set and the FM carrier running up and down the selectivity slope produces a detected signal varying in amplitude which the AM detector sees as normal AM. For lowest distortion the band-pass filter needs to be adjusted with the carrier approx 6dB down from the peak of the response so the carrier is swept up and down the filter slope. The exact side of the centre frequency is not critical; it can be either the lower skirt or the higher slope. For lowest distortion all the carriers in a multi-channel application should be on the same side of the filter slope. Because the filter is top coupled the upper slope will have a shallower response than the lower one and therefore will generate less phase shift per kHz of offset.

normally required in wide audio bandwidth broadcast FM transmitters where the highest modulating frequency is 15kHz, but not in telephony speech quality two-way radios where the maximum audio frequency is limited to 2.5kHz.

So the phase modulator inherently has the correct pre-emphasis of 6dB / octave if a flat audio response signal is applied. For data transmissions such as Packet radio AX25 protocol using Bell 202 tones of 1200Hz and 2200Hz a considerable improvement in sensitivity is obtained if the audio signal from the modem is a constant amplitude and the -6dB / octave de-emphasis is removed. For the 1200Hz tone the deviation is set to, say, 1.2kHz and when the 2200Hz tone is applied the deviation will be 2.2kHz. The receiver normally has a de-emphasis network following the demodulator for best SINAD performance. The output signal from the de-emphasis network will then be constant amplitude no matter which tone is transmitted.

For a transmitter using several channels widely spaced the centre frequency of the modulator can be varied to suit the exact crystal frequency by selecting the correct DC bias on the varicap diodes by switching different variable potential divider preset resistors with the channel switch feeding the +8V bias point. This will maintain a constant deviation and low distortion across the channels.

To adjust the phase modulator apply the oscillator signal and connect the output of the multiplier chain to a deviation meter and an audio distortion meter to the deviation meter AF out port. Apply a 1kHz audio tone of very low distortion to the modulator input and adjust L1 and L2 for the maximum deviation and then for the lowest distortion. Reduce the audio input to keep the deviation to 3kHz maximum as the inductors are adjusted. With care a distortion figure of less than 1% should be obtained.

Multi-channel crystal oscillator

When several crystals need to be switched for a receiver or transmitter the difficulty is arranging a circuit where the inactive oscillator crystals do not interfere with the active crystal. Using a multi-pole wafer switch often does not work satisfactorily because of the capacitance between adjacent switch wafers and the wiring between the switch and the crystals, especially if this is more than a few centimetres. The circuit shown in **Fig 8.12** gets around this problem by using individual oscillators that are switched by a DC supply via a wafer switch. The common emitter resistor, which the output signal is developed across, causes the non-active oscillators' coupling diodes (D1) to be reverse biased and this prevents the RF from the active oscillator causing the other oscillators to be parasitically driven and so generating spurious signals.

The circuit suits fundamental crystals with a shunt capacitance of approx 30pF. The active oscillator emitter current causes the voltage across R3 to reverse bias the coupling diodes D1. The circuit can accommodate as many oscillators as required and each one has individual crystal trimmers to set the crystal on frequency. Diodes D1 can be 1N914 or 1N4148

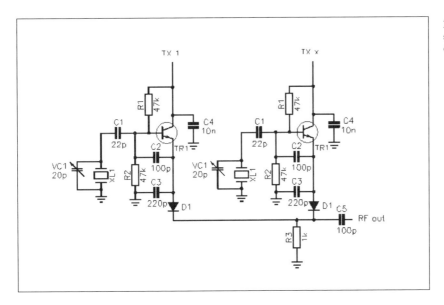

Fig 8.12. DC switched multi-oscillators

types. The diode reverse bias is about 3V when the DC supply rail is 8V. The oscillator output should be followed by a buffer amplifier for the best frequency stability and to isolate the oscillators from pulling by a subsequent modulator or multiplier stage.

The circuit shown in Fig 8.12 was designed to drive a phase modulator like the one shown in Fig 8.11. The DC switching circuit is shown in **Fig 8.13**. The 10-position wafer switch energises the individual oscillators and each output also feeds a preset pot to set the varicap diode bias. Diodes prevent back feeding. Only two oscillator switching is shown; the remainder follows the same logic. The diodes can be 1N914 or 1N4148 types, these serve to compensate the varicap diodes against changes in ambient temperature causing the oscillator RF level to vary as well as pre-

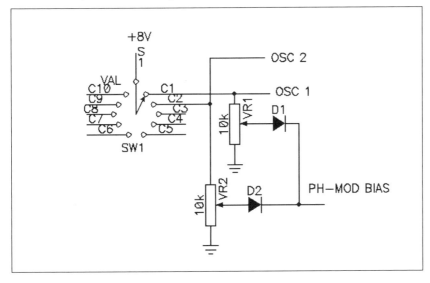

Fig 8.13. DC switching of oscillators and varicap bias adjustment

venting back feeding to the other inactive channels. The preset pots should be multi-turn types for fine adjustment. (For multi-channel applications resistor R2 is removed in Fig 8.11 to obtain the correct bias voltage on the varicap diodes.)

Once channel 1 has been aligned the inductors L1 and L2 are not touched. Begin by selecting channel 1 and setting VR1 to mid travel so that 4V is applied to the varicap diode bias point. Adjust the crystal trimmer to obtain the correct frequency. Apply a 1kHz audio tone of sufficient amplitude to obtain two-thirds the required peak deviation and adjust L1 and L2 for highest deviation consistent with lowest distortion. Adjust the audio level to maintain a deviation of two-thirds the peak deviation required. Select channel 2 and adjust VR2 to bring the distortion to the lowest reading, adjust the crystal trimmer for channel 2. Continue through the remaining channels adjusting the preset pots to get the lowest distortion for each channel and setting each crystal on frequency with the trimmer capacitor.

Having set all the channels for lowest distortion and correct frequency, switch through all the channels in turn and note the deviation obtained. If one channel shows a deviation figure substantially higher than the others adjust the audio level to obtain two-thirds the peak deviation on that channel. The higher the carrier frequency the more sensitive the modulator is, so we expect a channel near the top of the band to have the highest deviation. For the 2m band, where the FM activity is confined to a narrow portion of the band, this should not be a problem. This could, however, be corrected by having individual audio level preset pots for each channel by using a further wafer on the channel switch.

Simple high gain IF amplifier

For simple receivers often a high gain IF amplifier is required which can be controlled by automatic gain control (AGC). The circuit shown in **Fig 8.14** is a two-stage gain controlled amplifier constructed with low cost dual gate mosfets.

This is a straightforward manual gain controlled intermediate frequency amplifier and a detector suitable for AM and similar modes. The amplifier consists of two high-gain mosfets with AGC applied to gate 2 of each device. The overall gain is approx 70dB and the AGC range is of a similar level. The design frequency is 10.7MHz and the bandwidth is about 200kHz. For narrower band applications the use of a crystal filter before the amplifier will be needed. The input of the amplifier accepts a 50Ω source signal.

The detector uses a junction FET configured as an infinite impedance detector. This is a very good AM demodulator with low distortion of signals up to 100% modulation. For general use the audio can be filtered and fed into an audio amplifier. The signal appearing across the source resistor consists of a DC component, relative to the strength of the carrier, and the demodulated AM signal. The AGC voltage needs to be supplied externally and should swing from zero volts for minimum gain to +6V for

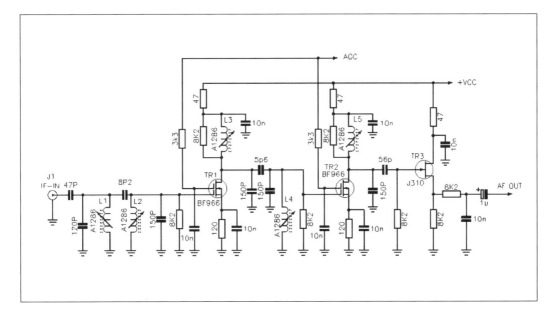

maximum gain. The supply voltage should be between 8V and 15V.

As the gain is high the layout needs to be carefully done. A double-sided board with the top foil used as a ground plane would be the best approach. The inductors have a nominal value of 1.25μH.

Fig 8.14. Gain controlled IF amplifier

Product detector for SSB or CW reception

When demodulating SSB or CW transmissions a product detector is the best option. The amplified IF amplifier signal is fed into another 'mixer' and a stable carrier at the IF causes a 'beat note' to be produced which is the difference between the IF signal and the stable carrier. This carrier is called

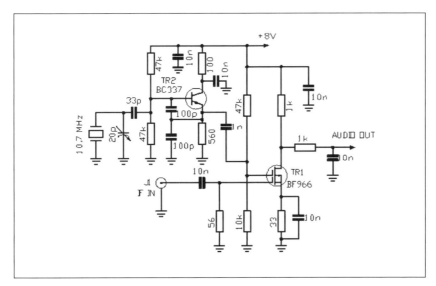

Fig 8.15. Product detector circuit

the 'Carrier Insertion Oscillator' (CIO) and for best results it should be produced by a crystal oscillator. The circuit shown in **Fig 8.15** uses two transistors to form a product detector.

The gate-1 resistor of TR1 should be chosen to suit the source driving the detector. In the schematic a 56Ω is shown which suits a 50Ω source. If the source is, for example, the IF amplifier shown in Fig 8.14, the signal can be tapped off from the final amplifier at a high impedance and coupled to the product detector with a gate-1 resistor of approx 47kΩ. The frequency of the crystal needs to be chosen to suit the IF signal.

A high performance log-amplifier

When the desire is for a very accurate S-meter in a receiver, a good option is to use a type of IF amplifier known as a 'logarithmic amplifier'. One such device is made by Analog Devices and is usable to 50MHz. This device is the AD-606 and features a log range of up to 90dB with a built in lift stage and video filtering. The block diagram of the AD-606 is shown in **Fig 8.16**. The log-amp output is a DC voltage which varies between 0.5V to approx 4V for the 90dB range, 3.5V = 90dB or 38.88mV per dB.

The IC needs very little in the way of components to provide a very accurate DC output versus RF input amplitude. This, however, is not the lowest cost method and we can use another commonly available IC from Philips Semiconductors to achieve almost as good a result.

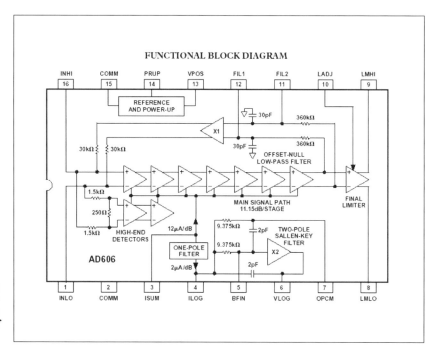

Fig 8.16. AD606 log amplifier block diagram (courtesy of Analog Devices)

A lower cost approach

A line up using log amplifiers is not the least expensive method of getting accurate amplitude information. Many of the modern ICs designed for wireless communication contain a similar type of measurement circuit.

In cellular telephone systems the base station needs to know the level of received signal from a handset to allow it to adjust the transmitter power to reduce inter-modulation in its multi-channel output stages. Handsets situated close to the base station do not require as much base transmit power to attain a good S/N ratio and hence transmit power can be turned down. The handset also contains an IF amplifier with a signal measuring device, which performs a similar function to adjust the handset transmitter power to conserve battery life and thus allows longer 'talk-time' between recharges. On the modern cell-phone the received signal level is displayed.

This method is known as 'RSSI' (Received Signal Strength Indicator). Many of the FM integrated circuits today contain some sort of RSSI circuitry, which although not as accurate as a true log-amp, are adequate for most amateur applications. A typical IC is the Philips NE-604/614. This is a conventional FM IC and contains circuitry to drive a quadrature detector with a good RSSI circuit. For our application the FM detection is not required, only the RSSI, which covers a range of 90dB. The bandwidth of the NE604 is limited to about 1MHz so the best option is to use it with a 455kHz IF which is converted down from either 10.7MHz or 21.4MHz. The application notes available from Philips detail the use as a measuring receiver and it has been used in several designs for an amateur spectrum analyser. The response of the RSSI is fairly slow with the standard circuit but if the NE624 version is substituted it can be speeded up to approx 2μs

Fig 8.17. Philips Semiconductors application circuit for the NE602 and NE604 (courtesy of Philips Semiconductors)

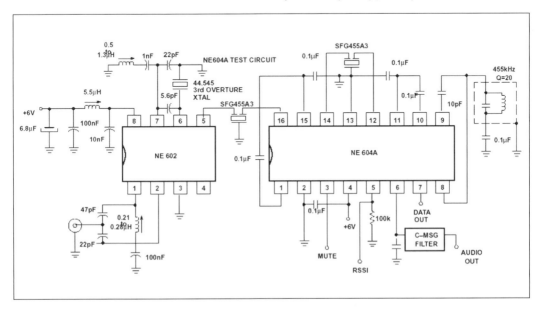

with suitable component substitution and a low pass post detection filter to reduce the quiescent noise.

The NE602 is a mixer IC designed for use up to approx 500MHz input frequency. The NE604 is a multi-stage FM limiting IF amplifier with a gain of approx 90dB and a good RSSI indicator. The response of the application circuit is shown in **Fig 8.18**.

For use as an S-meter we simply need to connect the NE602 input to the existing IF after the main crystal filter to limit the bandwidth. It is preferable if the IF used for the S-meter is different to the main IF to prevent spurious signals being generated. If the main IF in the receiver is, say, 9MHz then mixing down from this to 455kHz will give good results. If the main receiver IFs are for example 10.7MHz and 455kHz, using a different second IF for the RSSI circuit would entail a different second local oscillator frequency. If both IF amplifiers used 455kHz the limited 455kHz signal could leak into the other IF amplifier stages and cause a spurious beat.

The RSSI stage can be simplified because we do not need the FM demodulator components and these are omitted. Another of the Philips ICs is one that combines the NE602 and NE604 into a single package, the NE605/615. In use the two are the same, only the pin outs vary.

Fig 8.18. Typical performance of the application circuit

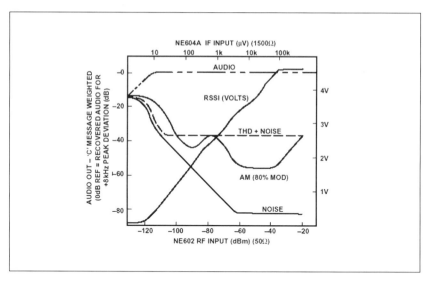

CHAPTER 9

Design of low-pass filters

In this chapter:

- Types of low-pass filter
- How a low-pass filter is characterised
- Component Q values
- Selecting the correct filter order
- How many poles are needed?
- Self resonant frequency of capacitors and inductors
- Standard low-pass filters
- Non-reflective harmonic filter
- High attenuation low-pass filters

T HE AVERAGE amateur transceiver contains many different filters to shape the RF spectrum. Some of these are low-pass filters (LPF), used for harmonic suppression, and some are high-pass or band-pass filters. Of the three main types the band-pass filter causes the most problems. Low-pass and high-pass filters are simple to design and make by consulting tables such as those found in Zverev's *Handbook of Filter Synthesis* [1].

The intention of this chapter is to show the amateur constructor the best topology to use for a particular application. By following these simple guidelines an amateur constructor will be able to design and build a filter with minimal effort and a good certainty of success.

> Anatol I Zverev, an engineer and formidable mathematician, moved to the USA after WWII and took up a position at Westinghouse Electric Corporation. His book published in 1967 is a classic textbook, now selling for about $300. Secondhand copies, in any condition, command a very high price.

Types of low-pass filter

There is a myriad of different types of low-pass filter in common use. These include the *Butterworth*, *Chebyshev* and the *Cauer-Chebyshev*, normally called the *Elliptic Filter*. Of the three main types the Chebyshev type allows the designer to select the ripple in the pass-band and hence the ultimate slope of the filter beyond the cut-off frequency. The Butterworth filter is almost never used. It features the lowest insertion loss ripple in the pass-band but the poorest roll-off in the stop-band. The Chebyshev types offer much steeper cut-off slopes and hence greater attenuation to the harmonic signals.

For low-pass filters intended for transmitter harmonic suppression the greater the ripple allowed in the pass-band the steeper the slope of the filter after the cut-off frequency is exceeded. In practice the ripple should not be allowed to become excessive or else the attenuation loss in the filter can reach unacceptable levels. Generally, a maximum ripple of 0.5dB is the figure most designers aim for, although many would prefer a lower value such as 0.1dB.

It must not be forgotten that most LC filters are what are known as 'reflective types', that is to say the filter prevents the unwanted radio frequency power (harmonic) from passing through the filter by generating a high VSWR at the input port and the output port at that frequency. For a transmitter this can give rise to instability at frequencies outside the pass-band if the transmitter design does not tolerate this high VSWR.

At frequencies far from the pass-band the filter reflects all the power back towards the transmitter output stage and presents an infinite VSWR to the transmitter. There are certain types of *non-reflective* low-pass filters we will examine later. These maintain a low VSWR irrespective of the frequency presented to the low-pass filter. However, the design of such a filter is more complicated.

How a low-pass filter is characterised

There are several parameters that define a low-pass filter. The first is the impedance the filter is designed to work into. For harmonic antenna filters this is normally 50Ω, although some transmitters are designed for a different impedance.

The second parameter is called the *stop-band*. This is the frequency above the normal band that will pass radio frequency power with little attenuation. The point at which the *cut-off* frequency is placed determines the transition between the pass-band and the stop-band. This cut-off frequency needs to be carefully selected. For most harmonic filters the choice of the cut-off frequency is critical. If the cut-off point is placed too close to the upper frequency range of the transmitter the insertion loss at this point can become excessive and a great deal of radio frequency power will be absorbed by the filter, causing excessive heating and a large drop in transmitted power. In the Butterworth filter the cut-off point is defined as 3dB down from the pass-band loss. In the Chebyshev types it is not so simple.

The third parameter is of course the pass-band, within which the transmitter is able to deliver maximum power with little insertion loss due to the attenuation in the filter. Because of the topology of the standard low-pass filter this normally extends from DC to the cut-off frequency.

Finally, the pass-band ripple defines how much additional attenuation is added to the inherent insertion loss of the filter. If the pass-band ripple is excessive, say 1dB, then we can expect the output power to drop by about 20% when the filter ripple increases the insertion loss to maximum. Most designers prefer to minimise the ripple to allow maximum power to be transmitted. But as already mentioned this has an effect on the ultimate cut-off region and the attenuation it is possible to obtain in the stopband. To achieve high values for the stop-band attenuation requires more components to be added which increase the pass-band insertion loss.

Component Q values

In an ideal filter the inductors and capacitors used to construct it would have Q values approaching infinity. In the real world this is often not realisable. The component with the lowest Q will dictate the insertion loss and the ultimate roll-off after the cut-off frequency is exceeded. In practice the component that normally limits the response is the inductor. The Q value of the capacitor is normally at least a factor of 10 greater than the inductors used. So if the inductor Q is poor the insertion loss will be higher and the ultimate attenuation to the harmonics will be less than possible.

In order to obtain high Q values for the inductors we need to use a wire that is substantial and has low DC resistance and *skin resistance.* In general, for high-power low pass filters, above about 50W, we will need to use 16SWG (1.6mm diameter) or thicker copper wire to manufacture the inductors.

As an example, an inductor for an HF transmitter harmonic filter will exhibit an unloaded Q of not much more than 500 if wound from a substantial gauge of wire. To achieve this Q value requires a large diameter, single layer, air dielectric solenoid winding, with the turns spaced at least one-wire diameter from the next turn. The optimum unloaded Q occurs when the length to diameter ratio is approx 1:1. So if the coil is 1 inch in diameter (25mm) the length should not exceed approx 1.2in (30mm). If the inductor is placed within two-coil diameters of a metallic shield it will severely *de-Q* the inductor. The high voltage RF capacitors used will normally have unloaded Q values of more than 2000. If the capacitor Q is poor they will heat up and in severe cases explode, so it is important to select these carefully. It must not be forgotten that very high values of circulating RF current will be flowing in both the inductors and the capacitors, in some cases as much as 50A for a 400W transmitter.

Selecting the correct filter order

The number of components used in a filter is known as the *Filter Order.* So if a low pass filter consists of three inductors and four capacitors there are a total of seven components, known as *poles.* This is therefore known as a *seven-pole filter.*

The greater the number of poles used, the steeper the cut-off slope will be, but at the expense of a slightly greater insertion loss. For standard Chebyshev filter types the best performance is obtained when the filter has

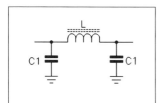

Fig 9.1. Three-pole low-pass filter

an odd number of poles, hence three-pole, five-pole, seven-pole etc are the order of the day. It is possible to design an even number of poles but the component values become impractical beyond a certain point, or as a colleague once commented, "a six inch nail and a 10,000µF capacitor".

Fig 9.1 shows the most basic low-pass filter, using three poles. This is often referred to as a π-section ('pi-section') and a typical filter will be built up from several sections connected in series to achieve the required stop-band attenuation.

For a low-pass filter where the input and output impedance are the same, the value of C1 will also be the same at both ends of the filter. The value of C1 and L will depend on the operating frequency, system imped-ance and the desired cut-off frequency. The filter is symmetrical and be-cause the input and output impedance are the same it does not matter which way around the filter is placed in the circuit. For the rarer case where the input and output impedance are *not* the same, the values of C1 will be different as will the value of L for a particular frequency, and the filter must be connected the correct way around. An example of this might be a 50Ω transmitter feeding a 75Ω transmission line for a half-wave dipole antenna.

The frequency response of a three-pole filter is shown in **Fig 9.2**. You will notice the rather poor roll-off above the upper pass-band frequency. This due to the limited number of poles being used. The filter is designed to pass a band of frequencies from 0 to 10MHz. The attenuation at 50MHz is about 35dB. In this example the attenuation in the stop-band is 35dB at a

Fig 9.2. Re-sponse of a 10MHz three-pole filter

point that is five times the cut-off frequency. Hence, we can calculate the attenuation as being 35/5 = 7dB / octave. So at 20MHz we would expect to see an attenuation of approx 14dB, at 40MHz we would expect to see

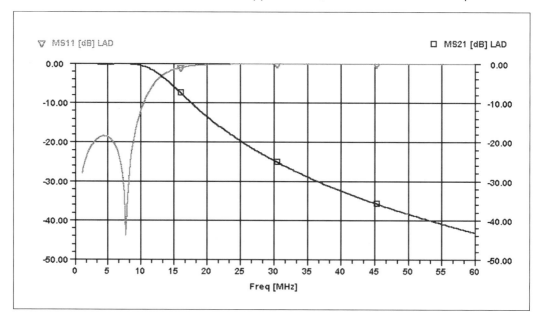

28dB, etc. In practice it is often not possible to make these assumptions as the inductors and capacitors at some very high frequency will exhibit self-resonant characteristics and become either parallel or series resonant.

In the Butterworth filter (known as the *maximally flat* filter because it inherently has no ripple in the pass-band) the attenuation is approx 6dB per pole per octave. So if the filter consisted of six poles it would have an attenuation of 36dB at twice the cut-off frequency and 72dB at four times the cut-off frequency. The Chebyshev types offer much greater attenuation in the stop-band than the Butterworth types.

How many poles are needed?

This very much depends on how much attenuation is required and how far removed from the cut-off frequency. Many constructors choose the number of poles rather unscientifically; even RF design engineers are sometimes guilty of this! How many poles are required depends on the spectral purity of the transmitter and what legislation it is necessary to comply with.

Let us take a transmitter and run it without a low-pass filter and measure the harmonic products. Suppose we use a 30MHz transmitter and drive it to its full output power and with a spectrum analyser measure the harmonic products. The second harmonic at 60MHz is likely to be the worst offender and the higher products at 90MHz, 120MHz and higher are usually less of a problem. The harmonic energy tends to fall off in a fairly linear manner. If the output stage of the transmitter consists of a push-pull topology the suppression of the even harmonics is normally better than the odd order harmonics. Hence, the second harmonic at 60MHz is usually better suppressed than the third harmonic at 90MHz. In a single-ended stage the suppression of the even and odd order harmonics is about the same and expected to drop off in a fairly linear manner.

Suppose we measure the second harmonic at 60MHz to be 30dB below the fundamental at 30MHz and the third harmonic at 90MHz to be 45dB below the fundamental. If the legislated specification is, say, below 60dB for all unwanted products then we can see that we require an additional 30dB at 60MHz but only an additional 15dB at 90MHz. If we simply took the 60dB specification and designed a filter with a minimum of 60dB attenuation at the second harmonic the filter would have far more poles and hence insertion loss than is required.

The order of the filter required, then, is not that high and a five-pole or seven-pole filter will probably fit the bill. It is preferable initially to select the lower filter order if possible to reduce the insertion loss at the 30MHz portion of the spectrum. Let us a design a five-pole filter and see what response we get. We will choose a 0.5dB ripple factor as this will ensure a faster roll-off above the cut-off point, and hence more attenuation at the 60MHz point on the response.

Fig 9.3. Five-pole Chebyshev filter

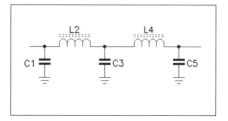

You will notice that the components are numbered from left to right and start with C1. This is a convention in a capacitor shunt - first element filter. The capacitors are given odd numbers and the inductors assigned even numbers. An alternative topology is to have a series inductor as the first element and the first capacitor in shunt to ground after the first inductor. Hence, there would be three inductors and only two capacitors. As the inductors generally need to be wound by hand, often it is better to choose the 'coil-saving design', with more capacitors and fewer inductors. In practice there is no difference in performance, but the smaller number of inductors often saves a considerable amount of effort and volume. In general the convention is for the shunt-connected components to be assigned odd numbers and the series-connected components to be assigned even numbers.

The cut-off point varies depending on the filter order; higher order filters require a smaller percentage. For a three-pole filter the cut-off percentage is approx 15%, for a five-pole filter it is approx 11%, for a seven-pole filter it is approx 9% and a nine-pole filter approx 7%.

The cut-off frequency for a five-pole filter hence needs to be placed at about 11% above the highest operating frequency, so in this case this puts it at 33.3MHz. By selecting the correct page in Zverev's tables we get the following values:

> N = 5, 0.5dB ripple, Z = 1, ω = 1
>
> C1 = 1.8068 Farad
> C3 = 2.6914 Farad
> C5 = 1.8068 Farad
> L2 = 1.3025 Henry
> L4 = 1.3025 Henry

Note that these are the *normalised* values and are in Farads and Henrys at a frequency of 1 radian/s and impedance of 1Ω. To convert to the design frequency we need to do some mathematical juggling. To convert the values to 50Ω we *divide* the capacitor values by 50 and *multiply* the inductor values by 50. This gives the following:

> C1 = 36.136 x 10^{-3} Farads
> C3 = 53.828 x 10^{-3} Farads
> C5 = 36.136 x 10^{-3} Farads
> L2 = 65.125 Henrys
> L4 = 65.125 Henrys

To convert to the required cut-off frequency of 33.3MHz we need to find the value of $2\pi f$. In this case this is 209.23 x 10^6. The rule is that the capacitors and inductors are then *divided* by the constant. So for our filter we end up with the following circuit values:

134

C1 = 172.8pF
C3 = 257.3pF
C5 = 172.8pF
L2 = 0.311µH
L4 = 0.311µH

As you can see, the filter is symmetrical and C1 and C5 are the same value, as are L2 and L4, because the input and output impedances are the same. It is important to use the values calculated and not to make large value substitutions. The 172.8pF may be made up from a 150pF and a 22pF in parallel. The 0.8pF error is not going be an issue. If however, the 172.8pF value was substituted by a 180pF this will cause the response to be incorrect with more insertion loss, ripple in the pass-band and a less steep roll-off.

The 257.3pF may be made up from a 220pF and a 39pF in parallel; or with two 120pF and 18pF, the small error resulting is not going to be too serious. The inductors in any case will need to wound to the exact values and then adjusted in circuit, preferably with the prototype filter measured on a sweep generator or network analyser to get the correct response. When constructing a filter it is also important to minimise the mutual inductance between adjacent inductors. The best method is to mount the inductors so that they are at 90° to each other. Shielding plates fixed between the inductors will also reduce the mutual coupling to very small values. Alternatively for a low power filter we could use inductors wound on low permeability ferrite toroidal cores. As toroidal cores are inherently self-shielding this make the filter compact.

If we now analyse the filter with the above values we see that the response looks like that shown in **Fig 9.4**. The insertion loss remains

Fig 9.4. 30MHz five-pole low-pass filter response

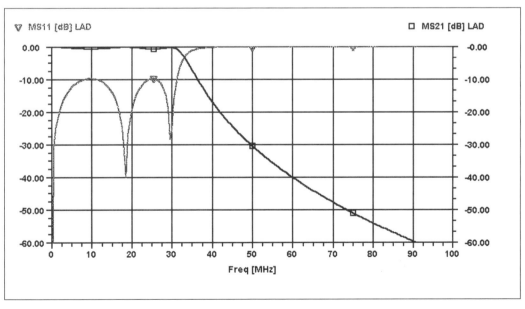

substantially flat from DC to 30MHz with a very small amount of ripple. Here we see that we have achieved our objective of 30dB attenuation at 60MHz, in fact the response passes through the 30dB point at 50MHz so we have some attenuation in hand. The attenuation at 90MHz is greater than 50dB, although we only required 15dB to meet the harmonic specification. The trace shows the input match as the magnitude of S_{11} (input reflection coefficient or input VSWR), between 0MHz and 30MHz. It is very low and as to be expected becomes very high beyond the cut-off frequency. The value at 30MHz is -27dB, which is a VSWR of 1.08:1. The ripple in the pass-band can be seen and the response kicks up to minimum attenuation towards the top of the pass-band. This is typical of a Chebyshev response filter. If you look closely you will see the worst VSWR occurs when the insertion loss ripple is at its worst and the best VSWR is when the ripple falls to zero.

If we had estimated the required filter order as being higher, say a seven-pole filter, we would have more insertion loss in the pass-band, hence less available output power into the antenna and much more attenuation in the stop-band, which we did not really require.

The inductor Q assumed in this simulation is only 50. The capacitors are assumed to have infinite Q. In practice we would choose a much higher Q for the inductors. With a Q value of 50 the maximum insertion loss is approx 0.6dB, which may be too high for some applications. If we now model the filter with a more practical Q value of 250 we can see the maximum insertion loss will go down. It drops to 0.5dB (10%) because this is the maximum ripple value chosen; the minimum insertion loss is 0.018dB. If we were concerned about power loss in the filter we could select a lower ripple figure, say, 0.1dB. Then the maximum insertion loss would be approx 0.1dB in theory, but the filter will require more poles because the lower

Fig 9.5. Expanded plot of pass-band ripple

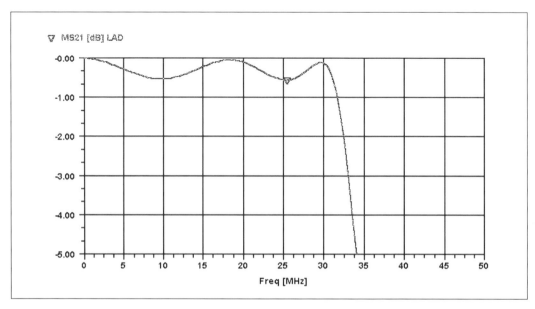

ripple filter has a less steep roll-off above the cut-off frequency.

It is impractical to increase the *pole order* in units of one, as this would become a six-pole filter and as has already been explained this tends to lead to impractical values. Hence, the next logical filter would be a seven-pole.

In practice as long as the 11% cut-off rule is observed the lowest insertion loss will normally occur just before cut-off, which in this case is between approx 28 and 30MHz, so suiting a 10m-band transmitter perfectly.

In order to examine the pass-band ripple more closely, the plot in **Fig 9.5** shows it on a 0 to 5dB vertical scale. As is to be expected, the ripple in the pass-band is ≈0.5dB.

We can tell this is a five-pole filter by counting the number of peaks and troughs from DC to the cut-off point. There are three peaks and two troughs, five in total; hence it consists of five poles.

Self resonant frequency of capacitors and inductors

When constructing a filter it is well to remember that the capacitor inherently has some self-inductance apart from the lead lengths. If the leads are excessively long the lead inductance cancels out part of the capacitance and makes the capacitor appear to have a lower value. A good estimate is 1nH of inductance for each mm of lead length. So if we used a lead length of 2mm on each lead of the capacitor it amounts to an additional 4nH apart from the internal inductance, which might be as much as 5nH for a ceramic disc capacitor.

For high power filters the best choice of capacitor is either compressed mica types such as Semco [2] or ceramic high voltage types made by ATC [3]. These are available in working voltages up to 600V DC and the RF voltage rating can be safely assumed to be of the same order. Both of these capacitor types are usable to the upper UHF spectrum, indeed they need to behave as real capacitors in a harmonic filter if they are going to act like a short circuit to the higher order harmonic energy. The inherent self-inductance of the Semco and the ATC types is for all practical purposes zero, provided the capacitor is soldered directly to a low inductance ground plane. Silver mica disc capacitors are hard to find today and are a poor substitute for Semco or ATC types. They have much higher self-inductance than the other types and relatively poor Q values.

Similarly the inductor will at some very high frequency exhibit a parallel resonant characteristic as the stray inter-turn capacity causes the inductor to become resonant.

Standard low-pass filters

Whereas it is relatively simple to design a low-pass filter from scratch using Zverev's tables, it is the writer's common method to calculate for a standard frequency of 1MHz and then to scale the filters accordingly. Hence, once the tedious calculations have been done for each filter order and ripple factor it is only necessary to make some simple calculations to ascertain

Table 9.1. Table
of standard low-
pass filters

the values for any other cut-off frequency. If for example a filter is required
for a cut-off of 100MHz, the 1MHz values for each component are simply
divided by 100.

Three-pole Chebyshev, Fc = 1MHz, Z = 50Ω

Ripple	C1, C3	L2
dB	pF	µH
0.5	5932.023	10.189
0.1	4560.744	12.682
0.01	3759.558	14.494

Five-pole Chebyshev, Fc = 1MHz, Z = 50Ω

Ripple	C1, C5	C3	L2, L4
dB	pF	pF	µH
0.5	5751.223	8566.992	10.365
0.1	4142.167	7133.643	12.381
0.01	3108.614	6482.700	13.408

Seven-pole Chebyshev, Fc = 1MHz, Z = 50Ω

Ripple	C1, C7	C3, C5	L2, L6	L4
dB	pF	pF	µH	µH
0.5	5696.474	8650.708	10.314	14.241
0.1	4015.479	7127.595	12.093	13.372
0.01	2905.214	6372.882	12.690	14.884

Nine-pole Chebyshev, Fc = 1MHz, Z = 50Ω

Ripple	C1, C9	C3, C7	C5	L2, L8	L4, L6
dB	pF	pF	pF	µH	µH
0.5	5672.919	8645.932	8828.006	10.282	11.079
0.1	3961.685	7072.845	7307.440	11.950	13.392
0.01	2818.316	6243.330	6594.426	12.345	14.814

Note: If the need is for system impedance other than 50Ω, the reader needs to
recalculate the *denormalised values*. If the system impedance was 75Ω the
capacitor values would be *divided* by (75/50) = 1.5 and the inductor values *multi-
plied* by the same figure to attain the correct reactance.

Non-reflective harmonic filter

For applications where the input VSWR presented to the source must remain low, another circuit topology is used. In this case the filter actually
consists of two filter types. One is the conventional Chebyshev low-pass
filter and the other is a Chebyshev high-pass filter. The two filters are connected together at the input of the filter and each filter feeds a separate
load. The low-pass filter connects to the antenna port, and the high-pass

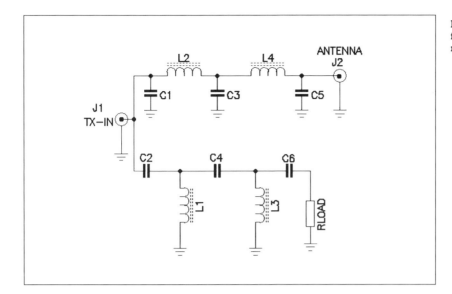

Fig 9.6. Non-re-
flective har-
monic filter

filter connects to a terminating load resistor.

The RF spectrum within the filter pass-band is all passed to the antenna port. The RF spectrum containing the harmonic energy is passed only via the high-pass filter and is dissipated in the terminating load resistor. The cut-off point of the two filters is chosen to be the same frequency. As the low-pass filter rolls off the power passing through it, the high-pass filter begins to roll down in insertion loss towards zero. Hence, the worst input match occurs at the cut-off point and returns to a low VSWR at frequencies removed from the cut-off point. With correct design the input match can be kept below 1.5:1 VSWR across the band from DC to some very high frequency. This circuit configuration is often called a *diplexer*. The basic configuration is shown in **Fig 9.6**.

The low-pass filter consists of a five-pole type and the high-pass filter also consists of a five-pole type. They do not have to be the same order. The high-pass filter consists of C2, C4, C6 and L1 and L3. The load resistor is the same as the system impedance, typically 50Ω. It need only have a power dissipation equivalent to the total harmonic power contained in the unwanted products. If the transmitter was rated at 100W and the second harmonic before filtering is 20dB below the fundamental the power contained in the harmonic is approx 1W. Hence, a 2W resistor would suffice in most cases.

High attenuation low-pass filters

In many applications the need is for more attenuation at the harmonics than a standard Chebyshev filter can provide. In this case a modification of the standard Chebyshev filter is used. This filter is known as the *Cauer-Chebyshev* or 'elliptic' filter. In essence it is a normal Chebyshev response but additional *zeros* are placed in the response with parallel resonant 'traps'.

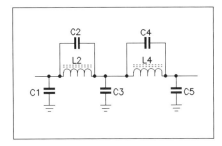

Fig 9.7. Cauer-Chebyshev elliptic filter

The basic configuration is shown in **Fig 9.7**.

In the diagram C2 and L2 resonate to provide a parallel resonant trap at one of the harmonics and C4 and L4 provide another trap at another harmonic. In practice the second and third harmonic are often chosen as these contain the greatest harmonic energy. The response of the elliptic filter is a very steep roll-off until the first notch frequency is reached, then a more gradual re-entry of the attenuation curve. The response of a typical elliptic filter is shown in **Fig 9.8**; the third harmonic notch is off the scale to the right. This filter is designed for a 50MHz transmitter where the possibility of interference to FM broadcast receivers operating around 100MHz is a common problem. The attenuation at 100MHz is approx 70dB. The filter is a conventional five-pole Chebyshev with two traps, so there are seven components used. With the elliptic filter attenuation values of approx 80dB per octave are readily achieved up to the first notch frequency. A normal five-pole filter would only achieve about 40dB.

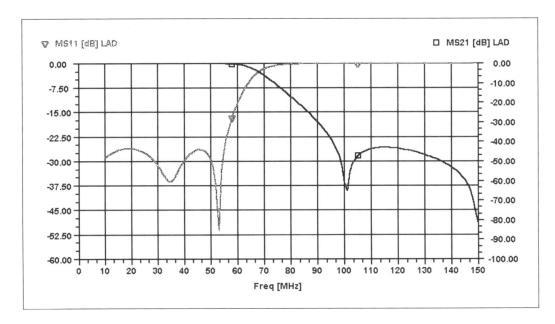

Fig 9.8. Elliptic filter response

Footnotes

[1] Published by John Wiley & Sons Inc., ISBN 0-471-74942-7.
[2] Silvered Electronic Mica Company, Willimantic, CT, USA.
[3] American Technical Ceramics Corp, Huntington Station, NY, USA.

CHAPTER 10

Design of high-pass filters

In this chapter:

- Basic high-pass filters
- Standard high-pass filters
- Converting a low-pass filter file to a high-pass filter

T HE HIGH-PASS filter is simply an inverted mirror image of the low-pass filter. In the high-pass filter the inductors are connected in shunt to ground between the series signal path. The series signal path consists of capacitors connected in series between the input and output.

Basic high-pass filters

A basic high-pass filter (HPF) with three-poles is shown in **Fig 10.1**. We can work out that this is a high-pass filter from first principles if we remember how the different reactances work. For capacitive reactance at DC the reactance is infinite, falling towards zero as the frequency increases. For inductive reactance it is zero at DC and rises towards infinity with increasing frequency.

As with the low-pass filter, if the input and output impedance are the same, the value of C will also be the same. The

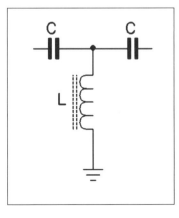

Fig 10.1. Three-pole high-pass filter

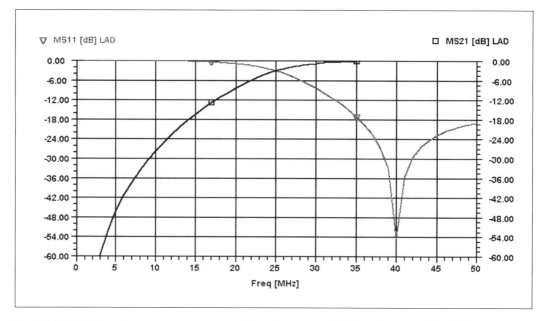

Fig 10.2. 25MHz cut-off three-pole HPF

frequency response of the three-pole HPF is shown in **Fig 10.2**.

In order to demonstrate the various types of filter order we will also use a 25MHz cut-off for all the following plots. We will choose 0.1dB ripple in the pass band and design for 50Ω impedance. You will notice that the curves of S_{11} and S_{21} cross at the cut-off frequency. In this filter the pass-band attenuation at the cut-off point is exactly 3dB below the zero insertion loss portion, the same as a Butterworth type. The point at which the insertion loss drops to zero in this example is approx 33MHz. This is about 13%

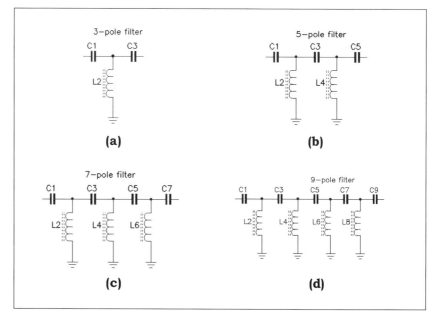

Fig 10.3. (a) three-pole, (b) five-pole, (c) seven-pole, (d) nine-pole high-pass filters

higher in frequency than the cut-off point. This agrees quite well with the 11% rule used for the low-pass filter types discussed in Chapter 9. As the filter order rises the cut-off point in percentage also drops towards zero, just like the low-pass filter. In practical filters (those below 11th order) it will always be above approx 2%.

Fig 10.4 (below). 25MHz five-pole HPF

Now look at the next two plots for a five-pole and a seven-pole version of the HPF (**Fig 10.4** and **Fig 10.5**).

You will notice that the curves of S_{11} and S_{21} all cross at the cut-off

Fig 10.5 (bottom). 25MHz seven-pole HPF

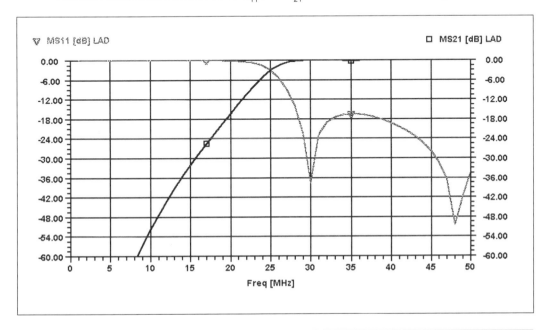

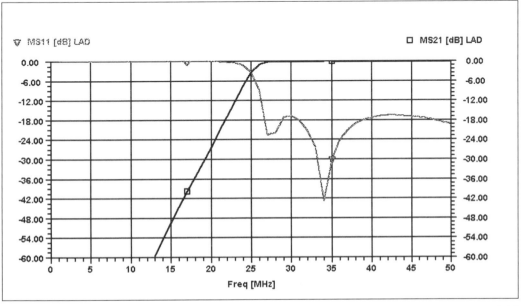

Three-pole high-pass filter, Fc = 1MHz, Z = 50Ω

Ripple	C1, C3	L2
dB	pF	μH
0.5	1708.038	6.215048
0.1	2221.593	4.993253
0.01	2695.029	4.369028

Five-pole high-pass filter, Fc = 1MHz, Z = 50Ω

Ripple	C1, C5	C3	L2, L4
dB	pF	pF	μH
0.5	1761.733	1182.693	6.109595
0.1	2446.091	1420.329	5.114562
0.01	3259.368	1562.947	4.722979

Seven-pole high-pass filter, Fc = 1MHz, Z = 50Ω

Ripple	C1, C7	C3, C5 pF	L2, L6	L4
dB	pF	pF	μH	μH
0.5	1778.665	1171.247	6.139764	5.746495
0.1	2523.265	1421.534	5.236738	4.735627
0.01	3487.564	1589.880	4.990122	4.25457

Nine-pole high-pass filter, Fc = 1MHz, Z = 50Ω

Ripple	C1, C9	C3, C7	C5	L2, L8	L4, L6
dB	pF	pF	pF	μH	μH
0.5	1786.050	1171.894	1147.724	6.158770	5.715951
0.1	2557.528	1432.538	1386.548	5.299159	4.728592
0.01	3595.097	1622.871	1536.467	5.129728	4.274682

Note: To scale to a higher frequency simply *divide* all the values by the new frequency. For example, for 100MHz, divide all the values by 100. To scale to another impedance, modify the values by the *ratio* of the new impedance to 50Ω. For example, for 300Ω impedance we would *multiply* all the inductor values by six and *divide* all the capacitor values by six.

Table 10.1. Table of standard high-pass filters

point of 25MHz. The main difference between the three plots is the steepness of the slope from the stop-band to the pass-band. All the vertical scales are a maximum of 60dB attenuation. The five-pole filter reaches zero attenuation at approx 29MHz and the seven-pole at approx 26MHz. The stop-band 60dB points are 3MHz for the three-pole version, 8MHz for the five-pole version and 13MHz for the seven-pole version. If we were to use a nine-pole version, the 60dB point would be reached at approx 20MHz.

The pass-band insertion loss is essentially zero, with a maximum value only slightly above the ripple factor chosen of 0.1dB. The pass-band insertion loss is dependent on the Q of the inductors and capacitors. If the Q is low the insertion loss will be higher. The pass-band theoretically extends to infinity, in practice at some very high frequency the inherent self-inductance of the capacitors and the stray capacitance of the inductors will modify the response.

In the stop-band the attenuation at DC is infinite. For the three-pole version it reaches 90dB below the pass-band at approx 1MHz. For the five-pole version 90dB down is reached at approx 4MHz and the seven-pole version reaches the same point at approx 8MHz.

Standard high-pass filters

The high-pass filter can be easily designed with the use of Zverev's tables. Again, I prefer to design standard filters with a 1MHz cut-off and then to scale these to the required frequency. These standard filters are listed in **Table 10.1** opposite. All have a 1MHz cut-off and impedance of 50Ω.

Converting a low-pass filter file to a high-pass filter

Often only values for low-pass filters are published. It is very simple to convert from one type to the other. The example below illustrates this.

The values for a five-pole low-pass filter with a 0.1dB ripple are listed below:

$$C1 = 1.3013$$
$$C3 = 2.2411$$
$$C5 = 1.3013$$
$$L2 = 1.5559$$
$$L4 = 1.5559$$

These are the normalised values in Farads and Henries at 1Ω impedance and a frequency of 1 radian/s.

To convert to a high-pass filter we take the reciprocal of the low-pass values. For example, the capacitors in the high-pass filter are C2, C4 and C6 and the inductors L1 and L3.

$$C2 = 1/C1 = 0.7684623 \text{ Farad}$$
$$C4 = 1/C3 = 0.4462095 \text{ Farad}$$
$$C6 = 1/C5 = 0.7684623 \text{ Farad}$$
$$L1 = 1/L2 = 0.6427148 \text{ Henry}$$
$$L3 = 1/L4 = 0.6427148 \text{ Henry}$$

Now we convert to 50Ω by dividing the capacitors by 50 and multiplying the inductances by 50:

145

C2 = 0.0153692 Farad
C4 = 0.0089242 Farad
C6 = 0.0153692 Farad
L1 = 32.13574 Henry
L2 = 32.13574 Henry

Now all we need to do is to convert to the required cut-off frequency. We do this by dividing the values by $2\pi f$. For a 100MHz cut-off this is 6.2832×10^8. The values become:

$C2 = 2.4461 \times 10^{-11} = 24.461pF$
$C4 = 1.4203 \times 10^{-11} = 14.203pF$
$C6 = 2.4461 \times 10^{-11} = 24.461pF$
$L1 = 5.1146 \times 10^{-8} = 51.146nH$
$L3 = 5.1146 \times 10^{-8} = 51.146nH$

CHAPTER 11

Design of band-pass filters

In this chapter:

- Cohn band-pass filter
- Scaling frequency

I N MANY items of amateur equipment we need symmetrical band-pass filters. Whereas there are many different types to choose from, only one topology suits the home constructor. This is the bottom-coupled 'Cohn filter', named after its inventor.

Cohn band-pass filter

The basic Cohn filter is shown in **Fig 11.1**. In order to make life easier I have calculated the component values for a range of frequencies and optimised the filter response and insertion loss using standard E12 capacitor values

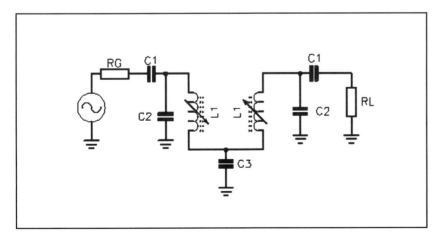

Fig 11.1. Cohn band-pass filter

with a complex analytical software package. This somewhat compromises the ultimate response but the results are still very acceptable.

The advantage of the bottom coupled Cohn filter is that the slopes are far more symmetrical than other types and they offer superior rejection to frequencies below and above the centre frequency. The criterion chosen was to obtain 40dB or more rejection at frequencies 20% either side of the centre frequency. In most cases the in-band insertion loss is less than 6dB. This assumes the Q of the inductor is adequate. I have used a Q value of 100, which is quite practical for inductors wound on toroidal cores.

Not obvious from the schematic is that the inductors must be well shielded from each other. The coupling between the two inductors is solely via C3. If the inductors are coupled magnetically (mutually coupled) the response will be different. Therefore the inductors should be types mounted in screening cans or wound on toroidal cores that offer good shielding. Positioning the toroidal cores at 90° to each other will give the least magnetic coupling.

The value of C3, the bottom coupling capacitor, affects the insertion loss and skirt selectivity. Lowering the value of C3 will reduce the insertion loss but cause the skirts to rise and offer less rejection. Taken to extremes the response will become double-humped due to over-coupling. Similarly, increasing the value of C3 will increase the insertion loss, narrow the pass band and cause the skirt slopes to fall off quicker, so obtaining more rejection at the expense of a narrower pass-band response. If this is carried too far the input and output match will suffer so it is best to stick within 10% of the calculated values for optimum performance. This can be corrected by altering the values of C1, C2 and L1 but needs complex analytical software to see the effect these have.

If you require greater rejection, two filters can be cascaded with a

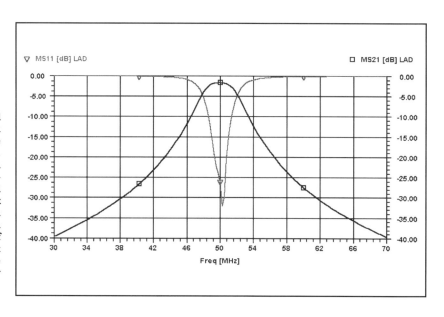

Fig 11.2. Typical attenuation response for the standard filters. The plot is for a 50MHz band-pass filter and shows approx 3dB insertion loss and a rejection of approx 37dB at 20% from the centre frequency

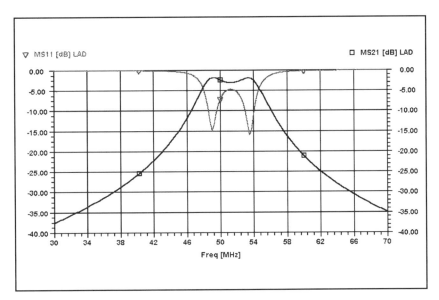

Fig 11.3. Over coupled filter response (C3 too small)

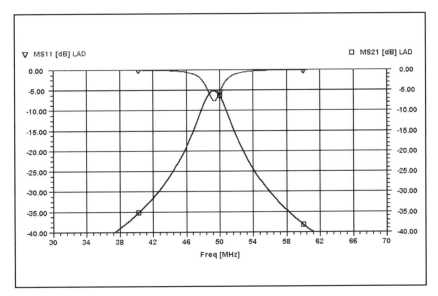

Fig 11.4. Under coupled response (C3 too large)

buffer amplifier inserted between the two. This will yield a rejection of approx 80dB at the 20% frequency points. Cascading by directly coupling two filters together will result in a skewed response because the filters will not be correctly terminated. A good amplifier to use is a 50Ω MMIC.

The component values are listed in **Table 11.1** for frequencies from 10MHz to 100MHz. By using these values when scaled we can select the correct values for other frequencies with a fair degree of certainty the filter will work correctly. The filters are designed for 50Ω impedance.

Table 11.1.
Z = 50Ω. Attenu-
ation ≈40dB at
20% from centre
frequency

f MHz MHz	C1 pF	C2 pF	C3 pF	L1 µH Q = 100 min
10	39	68	2200	2.472
20	22	39	1120	1.213
30	15	27	820	0.706
40	10	22	820	0.518
50	8.2	22	820	0.348
60	5.6	15	680	0.350
70	4.7	12	560	0.32
80	3.9	12	560	0.255
90	3.9	10	470	0.230
100	3.3	8.2	390	0.227

Notes: 1120pF = 2 x 560pF in parallel.
L1 Inductance tuning range ±20%.
All filters optimised for lowest insertion loss, input / output return loss (VSWR) and stop-band attenuation using standard E12 capacitor values.

If you redraw the Cohn filter (**Fig 11.5**) you will see that it predominantly is a low-pass filter, and this explains the superior rejection to frequencies above the centre frequency. Traditional 'top-coupled' band-pass filters are inherently high-pass in nature and the higher frequency rejection is a lot poorer than the Cohn filter for this reason.

Fig 11.5. Redrawn Cohn filter

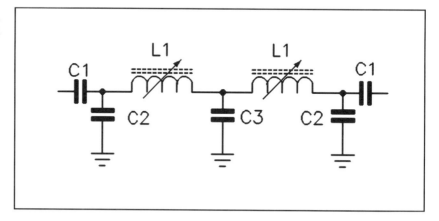

Scaling frequency

To scale to a new frequency, divide or multiply all values by the *ratio* of the new frequency to the old. For example, to make a 1MHz filter multiply all the values by 10 for the 10MHz design. To make a 200MHz filter, divide the

Table 11.2.
Standard E12
capacitor values

Base value pF	x 10	x 100	x 1000	x 10,000	x 100,000
0.1	1.0	10	100	1000	10000
0.12	1.2	12	120	1200	12000
0.15	1.5	15	150	1500	15000
0.18	1.8	18	180	1800	18000
0.22	2.2	22	220	2200	22000
0.27	2.7	27	270	2700	27000
0.33	3.3	33	330	3300	33000
0.39	3.9	39	390	3900	39000
0.47	4.7	47	470	4700	47000
0.56	5.6	56	560	5600	56000
0.68	6.8	68	680	6800	68000
0.82	8.2	82	820	8200	82000

Note: Values below 0.47pF are not normally available in standard capacitor types. Where very low value capacitors are required either a 'gimmick' capacitor, made from two insulated wires twisted together and pruned to length may be used, or a high value carbon-composition resistor. A 1MΩ 1/8W resistor has a parallel capacity of approx 0.2pF. Another alternative is to connect two or more capacitors in series, for example 2 x 0.68pF in series = 0.34pF.

the 100MHz values by 2.

Example: We need a filter with a pass-band centre of 15MHz. We would take the 10MHz filter values and divide all the values by 1.5. As we prefer to use E12 values if possible, this gives us the following new values:

$C1 = 26$pF	use 27pF
$C2 = 45.33$pF	use 47pF or 2 x 22pF in parallel
$C3 = 1466$pF	use 1500pF
$L1 = 1.648\mu$H	use value calculated

Alternatively, take the 30MHz design values and multiply by 2. This gives the following values:

$C1 = 30$pF	use 27pF or 2 x 15pF in parallel
$C2 = 54$pF	use 56pF or 2 x 27pF in parallel
$C3 = 1640$pF	use 2x 820pF
$L = 1.412\mu$H	use value calculated.

For frequencies in between the design standards we can interpolate the nearest E12 values (see **Table 11.2**). For example, we need a filter for 35MHz. By assessing the values at 30MHz and 40MHz we can choose suitable values:

C1 = 15pF at 30MHz	10pF at 40MHz	use 12pF
C2 = 27pF at 30MHz	22pF at 40 MHz	use 2 x 12pF in parallel
C3 = 820pF at 30MHz	820pF at 40MHz	use 820pF
L1 = 0.706µH at 30MHz	0.518µH at 40MHz	use ≈0.6µH

CHAPTER 12

Designing with valves

In this chapter:

- Valves vs solid state
- Valve emission
- Diodes and triodes
- Conductance (g_m) and voltage gain
- Grid current, grid bias and cut-off bias
- Tetrodes, pentodes and higher types
- Anode efficiency and anode dissipation
- Circuit losses
- Calculation of component values
- Operating classes: valve biasing
- Problems with capacitive coupled valve amplifiers
- Anode voltage waveforms for a RF amplifier
- Valve pin out details
- British receiving valve numbering system

T HE USE of valves by radio amateurs has declined over the years, except for RF power amplifiers, where their use is still widespread. Because the Radio Communications Examination syllabus no longer covers valves, many amateurs are unfamiliar with the parameters and characteristics of how valves work. This chapter is intended to cover the basics.

Valves vs solid state

The use of valves for high quality audio amplification has seen a revival over the last few years and many home constructors are now rediscovering the techniques largely lost over the period when transistor audio amplifiers ruled the roost. Not only are home constructors building valve audio amplifiers, but several well known companies are now offering hybrid amplifiers with solid-state low power stages and valve output stages, and in some cases completely valved amplifiers.

Many 'audiophiles' prefer the more 'rounded' quality of a valve amplifier. Transistor audio amplifiers tend to exhibit a harsh distortion when over driven on loud passages of music. Valves inherently have a softer limiting action and so do not *colour* the music as badly when a sudden loud transient occurs. The same can be said for receivers using valves, they tend to have better performance, in some cases far better than modern solid state versions, when handling strong signals because power handling is a fundamental property of the power that is being dissipated in the valve. Small signal transistor RF and IF amplifiers dissipate very little power and this factor limits their strong signal performance. In contrast, a valve receiver will be running something of the order of 2 to 5W per stage and this equates to superior strong signal performance, albeit at the expense of more power being drawn from the power supply and more heat to be dissipated. These, however, are not serious problems in most cases when the receiver is using the mains supply to power them.

Construction of valves

Valves are constructed in either a glass envelope for some types, or ceramic-metal envelopes or glass-metal for other types. (Some older style valves have a protective metal envelope over the normal glass envelope; these are largely obsolete today although they may turn up in older equipment). The envelope is evacuated so that a hard vacuum exists. The various internal parts of the valve are brought out to pins on the base and in some cases (normally only RF types) the anode or grid is a separate connection on the top of the glass envelope. Generally, low power and low frequency valves have all the connections on the base and RF power devices have the anode terminating on the top cap, although there are some exceptions to this rule.

Fig 12.1. Typical RF output valve (6146)

Valve emission

The basis of all valves is to generate free electrons by heating a structure called a *cathode*. This is made from a material that is heated to a high temperature and often coated with rare earth minerals that emit electrons freely when heated. The hot cathode develops a cloud of electrons around the cathode called a *Space Charge*. You can imagine it as being similar to water vapour hovering above the surface of boiling water. The electrons are boiled off from the cathode and remain in orbit for only a short time. They then lose energy and fall back to the cathode, but others will be launched to take their place. This is a continuous process and the average number of electrons hovering above the cathode is constant for a particular cathode temperature. This cloud of electrons is available to cause a flow of electric current. A current of 1A requires $\approx 6.25 \times 10^{18}$ electrons per second to be moved from one point to another. Electrons are negatively charged particles and will be repelled by another negatively charged electrode but attracted by a positively charged electrode we call an anode. Hence, electrons flow from the cathode to the anode, but in *conventional current flow* we say the current flows from the positive terminal to the negative terminal in a circuit. Hence, for simplicity we say the current flows from the anode to the cathode.

It is obvious that for a certain anode current to flow there need to be enough electrons available. If the surface area of the cathode is small or the temperature low, the number of electrons will be less. For high currents to flow we need lots of electrons being boiled off the cathode structure. Increasing the cathode area increases the number of electrons hovering and waiting to be attracted by the anode. Similarly raising the cathode temperature also increases the number of electrons hovering in the space charge.

Cathode heater and filament

However, there is a finite safe cathode temperature; exceed this and the whole cathode can melt and then the valve is useless. For this reason the manufacturers give maximum and minimum cathode heating currents and applied voltages which need to be observed for long valve life. For long life the heater voltage needs to be controlled to stay within about 10% of the nominal value. Some UHF and microwave valves suffer from *back-bombardment* where the electrons are moving so rapidly that they collide with the cathode or grid and give up their energy as heat. This raises the cathode and grid temperature and to counter this effect the filament current needs to be reduced. Some microwave triodes such as the 2C39 family can continue giving full emission when operated at full drive level so that the heater current can be turned off as long as the drive remains in place! Manufacturers normally give a recommended de-rating figure for the heater voltage for various frequencies when the valve is operated at full output power.

Some cathodes are *directly heated* and others are *indirectly heated*. The cathode has a resistance wire, often made from tungsten, through which a current is passed to raise the temperature. Directly heated cathodes use the heating filament as the cathode, the indirectly heated cathode has an insulated heating filament contained within a tube that causes the cathode to reach the required temperature. The filament may be supplied with either AC or DC and a convenient method is to derive this from a transformer with the necessary low voltage winding to suit the valve being used.

Some valves have dual-voltage filaments; these are two filaments connected in series. A tap point is provided so that a heater filament may be supplied one of two different filament voltages. For example many small valves have 6.3 + 6.3V AC filaments. For operation from a standard 6.3V AC filament transformer the two filaments are connected in parallel across the 6.3V AC winding. For operation from 12.6V AC or DC the filaments are connected in series using different pins on the valve base. In some equipment

The power absorbed by the heater can be quite high, a typical large amateur transmitting valve may require as much as 150W. Broadcasting valves running many kilowatts of RF output power may require several kilowatts just for the cathode heater. A typical transmitting triode such as the 3-500Z requires a 5V filament supply at 14.5A, hence 72.5W are drawn by the filament and this needs to be supplied by the transformer as does the anode current. If two valves are used the filament power required just to make the valves work correctly is 145W.

the heater filaments are connected in series and then fed from a higher voltage via a dropper resistor or transformer. Older television sets used valves with 19V or 23V filaments all having the same heater current and these where then connected across the 230V AC mains to eliminate the filament transformer.

Diodes and triodes

The simplest form of valve is a *diode*, which is short for *di-electrode* ('di' meaning two). This contains only two electrodes, the anode and cathode. If the anode is positive with respect to the cathode electrons will flow from the cathode to the anode. If, however, the anode is negative with respect to the cathode, the electrons - being also negatively charged - will be repelled and form a tight cluster around the cathode, and no current will flow. This two-electrode valve is therefore the basis of a rectifier and can be used to convert AC into DC.

In many rectifier diodes the cathode is directly heated and the filament transformer winding needs to be floating with respect to ground. In order to use a valve as an amplifier we need to include another electrode into the envelope. This is called a grid. This valve now contains three electrodes and is called a *triode*.

Triodes

The triode grid gives us a means to control the flow of electrons from the cathode to the anode. You can think of it like a tap placed in a water line, by opening or closing the tap we can regulate the flow of water. In hydraulics the tap is known as a *valve* and this is the reason we call valves 'valves'. The correct name is *Thermionic Electron Device* or TED, but nobody uses this today. Americans call valves *electron tubes* or simply tubes.

The grid is comprised of a fine mesh of wires placed close to and surrounding the cathode and connected to an external voltage source by a hermetically sealed pin exiting the valve envelope. In order for electrons to reach the anode they must travel through this grid mesh. If the grid has a small negative voltage applied it serves to repel the negatively charged electrons and prevent some of them from travelling through the grid mesh to the anode. If the grid voltage is sufficiently negative the flow of electrons ceases. By varying the grid voltage the flow of electrons which constitutes anode current can be varied in sympathy with the grid voltage. The grid in a triode is called the *control grid* because it allows the control of the anode current.

Fig 12.2. Diode valve rectifier

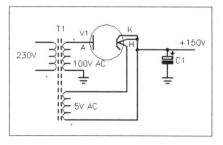

In order for a triode valve to amplify a signal voltage on the grid the anode needs to have a *load resistance*. If a fixed value resistor is connected from the anode to a positive supply voltage then the current flowing in the anode load resistor will cause a voltage drop given by Ohm's law. If the grid voltage is varied the anode current also varies and causes an AC voltage to be developed across the anode load resistor. This is the basis of all amplifiers using valves. A simplified triode amplifier is shown in **Fig 12.3**.

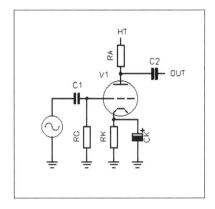

Fig 12.3. Basic triode amplifier

Conductance (g_m) and voltage gain

The triode valve with a varying grid voltage causes the anode voltage current to vary in sympathy. This is known as *conductance* (abbreviated g_m) and is expressed in mA/V. The mA portion is the anode current variation for a grid voltage change of 1V. A typical small signal triode might have a conductance of 5mA/V. Hence, if the input signal on the grid is varying by 1V the anode current will vary by 5mA.

In Fig 12.3 the anode is supplied via a resistor RA from a positive high voltage supply. The input AC signal is applied to the grid via a DC blocking capacitor C1 and a high value shunt resistor RG completes the DC path to ground. Resistor RK in series with the cathode to ground serves to establish the grid bias. Because the anode current also flows in RK this develops a voltage on the cathode which is positive to ground. The grid is connected via RG to ground so effectively the grid is now negative with respect to the cathode by the same voltage. If RK is 1kΩ and a current of 10mA flows the voltage between the cathode and ground is $V = I_a \times RK$ = +10V. Hence, the grid bias voltage is -10V with respect to the cathode. Capacitor CK is a low reactance to the AC signal and serves as a smoothing capacitor to maintain a constant DC voltage between the cathode and ground. The value of CK needs to be chosen so that it has at least 10 times less reactance compared with the value of RK. For audio frequencies this will require a large value electrolytic capacitor, perhaps 47µF or higher to cater for the lowest audio frequency.

The varying anode current flowing in RA causes an AC voltage to be developed across it. If RA is 10kΩ and the anode current varies by 5mA, the voltage developed across RA is 50V p-p. Hence, an input grid voltage swing of 1V p-p causes a 50V p-p signal to occur at the anode. The amplification is a function of the value of RA; if we increase RA to 20kΩ, the anode voltage swing is now 100V p-p for the same anode current variation of 5mA. The limitation to how far we can increase the value of RA is the available positive supply voltage and the peak anode current. If the valve is biased so that 10mA flows with no input signal, we can only swing the anode current down to about 2mA and up to 18mA before the signal becomes distorted. When the anode current is 2mA the anode voltage approaches the supply voltage. When the anode current swings up to 18mA the anode voltage will fall towards the cathode voltage.

We need a certain minimum anode-cathode voltage for the valve to operate correctly. Suppose this is 50V above the cathode voltage. If the supply voltage is 300V we can only swing between +50V and about +250V to ensure good linearity, a total swing of 200V p-p. If the cathode voltage is +10V due to RK, the anode can only swing down to +60V above ground. This now defines the value of RA more precisely and a suitable value resistor needs to be chosen that meets these requirements. Often the nearest E12 series resistor suffices with little error incurred.

Generally for lowest distortion when audio is amplified we will operate the valve in Class-A, where the anode voltage swing does not fall to zero on the positive excursion of the grid-cathode input voltage. From this we can see that the simple triode amplifier is an *inverting amplifier*. When the grid input voltage goes positive the anode current increases and the anode voltage falls towards zero. If the output signal needs to be in phase with the input, we need to connect a second amplifier in series to re-invert the waveform back to the correct phase.

Voltage gain

The simple triode amplifier is capable of high voltage amplification. Assuming the output load is high resistance then the voltage amplification is purely determined by RA and the positive supply voltage. For the example where RA is 20kΩ the voltage gain is 100 times if the load is infinity. If we connect two of these amplifiers in series the total voltage gain is 100 x 100 = 10,000 times. Hence, an input signal of 10mV p-p will develop an output voltage swing of ≈1V p-p into a load resistance that is much higher than RA, say 1MΩ. The grid resistor RG is often used to terminate a high impedance signal from a microphone; a piezo-electric microphone is typically 47kΩ to 1MΩ, so RG would be a similar value. Under small signal input conditions no grid current flows so RG can be chosen as any high value resistor convenient.

Grid current, grid bias and cut-off bias

When the input signal swing is large, the voltage swing may be enough to overcome the fixed grid bias voltage and then the grid is driven positive with respect to the cathode. The grid-cathode electrodes then behave like a rectifier diode, where the grid acts like an anode, and grid current will flow. The further the grid is driven positive with respect to the cathode, the greater the grid current.

When the input grid voltage swing is less than the bias voltage, the grid appears as an open circuit shunted by a small capacitance. The load the grid presents to the driving source is therefore negligible and the load is effectively the grid resistor placed between the grid and ground to complete the DC path for biasing. This can be a very high value to minimise the loading on the driving source.

If grid current flows it develops an additional negative bias voltage across the resistor RG, determined by the value of grid current and the value of RG. (Vg = Ig x Rg). For example, a grid current of 1mA flowing in a 100kΩ resistor will develop 100V of bias. When grid current flows, the grid-cathode rectifier shunts the grid resistance and it appears as a much lower effective value. This causes the loading on the driving source to change. In many RF amplifiers for CW or FM transmitters this method is used to develop the required grid bias. In this case the use of a cathode resistor is not required and the cathode can be tied directly to ground, which elimi-nates a potential source of instability due to the reactance of CK and any lead inductance associated with RK and CK. However, this means that if the drive signal falls below a certain level the grid bias will be insufficient to bias the valve correctly, and it may draw excessive anode current if the drive signal fails altogether. It is normally necessary to have either a small fixed bias voltage or some other method of reducing the anode current under a fault condition.

Fig 12.4. Anode current curves for the TD1-100C / 2C39BA triode

Grid bias

All valves intended for use as amplifiers (except Class-B zero-bias triodes) will require a grid bias supply to control the quiescent anode current. To reduce or cut off the flow of anode current the voltage applied between the grid and cathode of a valve needs to be a negative voltage with respect to the cathode. Hence, if the valve is operated in grounded cathode the grid voltage measured between ground and the grid terminal will be a negative voltage. However, if the valve is operated in grounded grid the cathode now becomes the input terminal and to bias the valve correctly the cathode needs to be positive with respect to the grid.

The valve manufacturers often supply graphs of anode current versus grid voltage for different operating anode voltages. Using these we can ascertain several parameters necessary when we are using a valve. A typical set of curves is shown in **Fig 12.4**. These are the curves for the popular 2C39BA microwave triode as supplied by

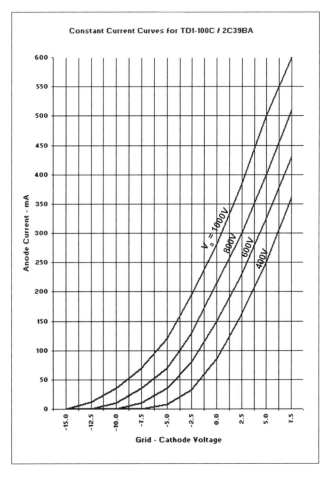

Note that the curves in Fig 12.4 are the average of several new valves, so some variation can be expected in practice. As a valve ages the grid bias voltage generally falls due to a decrease in cathode emission. As long as the bias supply has sufficient adjustment we should be able to obtain the correct quiescent current. For anode supply voltages other than the values given we can interpolate between adjacent curves to find the approximate grid bias voltage. For example, at 700V the grid bias required is about -6V for 50mA quiescent anode current.

Mullard in the data book published in 1969 for their TD1-100C version. These curves are obtained by varying the grid bias voltage using a DC supply and the various points are plotted on the graph. Under AC signal conditions the valve behaves in the same manner and the anode current will vary due to the varying grid voltage.

From these simple curves we can ascertain several important parameters. The horizontal axis is the grid to cathode voltage. The vertical axis is the anode current in mA. The curves show different anode voltages, ranging from 400V up to 1000V in 200V steps. These cover the range of voltages likely to be used. The manufacturers recommended maximum anode voltage is given as 1kV and the maximum anode dissipation is 100W when forced air-cooled.

The grid voltage scale runs from +5V to -15V, the anode current runs from 0mA to 600mA. If we need to find the correct biasing point with a particular anode voltage we can derive this from the curves. Let us firstly examine the anode current for different supply voltages when the grid bias is 0V. By drawing a vertical line at the point that corresponds to 0V we see that the line intersects the four curves at different places. For an anode voltage of 400V, the line intersects the curve at an anode current of 90mA. For the 600V curve it occurs at 150mA, for 800V at 220mA and for 1kV at 280mA.

The maximum safe anode dissipation is given as 100W, hence under these conditions the anode dissipation would be 36W for the 400V supply, 90W for the 600V supply, 176W for the 800V supply and 280W for the 1kV supply voltage. In order to stay within the 100W anode dissipation criterion for 800V and 1kV the anode current must be less than 125mA and 100mA respectively. For biasing the valve to a particular quiescent current we can use the same curves to ascertain the grid voltage required.

Suppose we need a quiescent anode current of 50mA. By drawing a line horizontally from the 50mA point on the vertical scale we can see where the line intersects the curves. We then drop a line down to intersect the horizontal scale and read off the grid voltage required. For the 400V anode supply we find we need approx -1.75V. Similarly for 600V we need -5V, for 800V we need -6.5V and for 1kV we need -8.5V.

Because the valve is operated in grounded grid the cathode voltage will be the same value but opposite sign, hence the cathode voltage required will be positive with respect to ground to achieve the correct bias voltage.

The other factors we can establish from these curves is the RF input voltage required to drive the anode current up to the required level. Suppose we are using an 800V supply and have biased the anode quiescent current to 50mA. By following the 800V curve we can ascertain the required grid voltage. If we need to drive the valve to 320W input this is an anode current of 400mA. We draw a horizontal line from the 400mA point until it intersects with the 800V curve. We now drop a vertical line to intersect with the horizontal axis and read off the grid voltage as +5V. As the quiescent grid voltage is -6.5V and we need to swing the grid up to +5V this is a total of 11.5V. When viewing this in cathode voltage it is from +6.5V to -5V. This voltage is the peak RF voltage required and when converted to rms we have a lower RF voltage of approx 8V rms across the cathode-grid terminal (11.5 x 0.707 = 8.13V rms).

Cut-off bias
During periods of receiving we need to cut-off the anode current to reduce dissipation and to prevent valve noise from interfering with reception. We could achieve this by disconnecting the high voltage supply but this re-quires a high voltage relay, which is inconvenient. A simpler method is to bring the cathode voltage higher in voltage to achieve the same result.

We can ascertain the required grid bias voltage to reduce the anode current to zero. Assuming we are using an 800V supply voltage we can find the required voltage to cut-off the valve. Following the 800V curve to the left we find that is crosses the 0mA anode current scale at approx -12.5V. This translates to a cathode voltage of +12.5V, as long as the cathode voltage is greater than +12.5V the anode current will be insignificant. A good choice would be +20V and a 20V 1W-zener diode connected between the cathode and ground would suffice. An alternative method is to use a high value resistor, say 100kΩ.

Tetrodes, pentodes and higher types
The tetrode valve contains four electrodes. As well as the anode, cathode and control grid there is an extra grid which is called the *screen grid*. The screen grid is placed between the control grid and close to the anode and is supplied with a positive voltage lower than the anode voltage.

Effectively what the screen grid does is to give some extra impetus and control to the electrons flowing towards the anode. When an electron is attracted towards the anode, which is a large distance from the cathode, the electron accelerates and as it approaches the anode it can reach very high velocity. Although the electron has very little mass it does have some. Due to the high velocity it attains, it is capable of giving up the energy it possesses as kinetic energy when it collides with the anode, which develops heat in the anode. When it collides with the anode, now travelling at a velocity close to the speed of light, it tends to dislodge other electrons. These would tend to travel back towards the control grid and partially reduce the total anode current. The screen grid, because it is also positively charged, acts as a 'catcher' and grabs the stray electrons bounced off the anode and diverts them back to the power supply. Hence, a higher rate of flow of electrons can occur than in the triode valve.

The screen grid often has additional electrodes formed in a funnel shape to deflect any errant electrons and so force them to travel towards the anode. These are known as 'beam-forming plates' and they increase

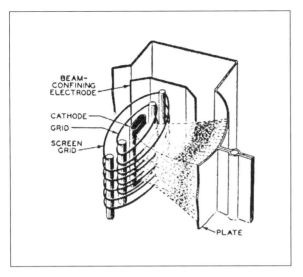

BEAM-
CONFINING
ELECTRODE

CATHODE

GRID

SCREEN
GRID

PLATE

Fig 12.5. Beam tetrode construction (from the RCA *RC-30 Receiving Tube Manual*)

the anode current flow. Consequently a tetrode has a higher conductance than a triode and will provide more output power for the same grid voltage swing; hence a tetrode has a higher gain. The screen grid is often known as *grid-2* or g2 and the control grid is known as *grid-1* or simply g1. In valve data sheets we see these referred to as Vg1 or Vg2 being the voltages applied to grid-1 and grid-2.

To cut-off a tetrode we have two options. Either we increase the grid bias voltage during receive or we remove the screen grid voltage and also connect the screen grid pin to ground. In most amplifiers both of these methods are used to ensure the valve is completely cut-off. The screen grid must never be left floating because it will charge up to a voltage close to the anode and cause a potential flashover within the valve envelope.

Pentodes and higher types

In the pentode valve we insert another grid between the screen grid and the anode. This grid is known as a *suppressor grid* because it is normally connected either internally to the cathode or this is performed externally by connecting the valve base pins together. This electrode is also known as *grid-3* or g3 for short.

The suppressor grid performs a similar screening function to the screen grid but as it has no potential difference to the cathode it serves to divert 'reflected' electrons from the anode directly back to the cathode.

Valves with more than five electrodes include the heptode, which contains six electrodes, and the octode with eight electrodes. These types are normally used for frequency mixers in receivers. By adding extra control grids we can supply two or more frequency signals to form the basis of mixing.

Anode efficiency and anode dissipation

No valve is perfect and so some of the DC input power is not converted into useful output power but is dissipated as heat in the valve. Part of this is the kinetic energy given up when the electrons slam into the anode structure at close to the speed of light; this causes internal heating, which can be destructive.

The usual way to express

Some high power valves' anode structures glow dull red or orange when running at the maximum rated anode current. This is normal and it is how the heat dissipated in the anode is conducted away by radiation. The valve being a hard vacuum cannot conduct heat except by radiation.

this is in terms of anode efficiency:

$$\text{Anode Efficiency} = \frac{\text{RF output}}{\text{DC input}} \times 100\%$$

where the RF output is power in watts
DC input is the anode current x the anode voltage.

A typical Class-C RF amplifier will have an efficiency between 50 and 75% depending on the operating frequency. At low frequencies the efficiency is often 60% or more, but at UHF and microwaves the efficiency falls and may even be as low as 20% in a practical amplifier. Hence, a large portion of the DC input power is wasted as heat in the anode and this determines the allowable DC input power.

For example, an amplifier for 80m (3.5MHz) delivers 100W carrier output power for an anode current of 200mA with an anode supply voltage of 750V. The valve chosen has a maximum anode dissipation of 60W. The DC input power is 0.2A x 750V = 150W. The efficiency is:

$$\text{Anode Efficiency} = \frac{100}{150} \times 100\% = 66.66\%$$

The power dissipated in the anode is (150 - 100) = 50W. As this is less than the 60W anode dissipation we can see the valve is operating within its safe limits.

Now consider a microwave amplifier operating at 2.3GHz. Anode efficiency and other circuit losses can cause poor conversion efficiency. For the popular 2C39BA the maximum recommended anode voltage is 1kV and an anode dissipation of 100W when forced air-cooling is used. The anode current is 250mA at 1kV and the output power is 50W. The DC input power is therefore 250W.

$$\text{Anode Efficiency} = \frac{50}{250} \times 100\% = 20\%$$

The DC input power is 250W and only 50W are delivered to the load, so 200W are dissipated in the anode. This is twice the manufacturer's recommended anode dissipation and will cause a high anode temperature and a shortening of the valve life if operated continuously at full carrier. In order to stay within the manufacturer's anode dissipation rating of 100W we can only expect about 25W of output power for this amplifier if full carrier operation is required, e.g. FM transmissions. This assumes that sufficient air is forced through the anode cooling fins.

However, if the amplifier is used for Morse code keyed transmis-

Many microwave triodes used by amateurs were originally developed for radar applications or pulsed duty. If the time for which the valve develops power is very short and the time between adjacent transmit pulses is long, the average power drops significantly. For example, the popular 2C39BA microwave triode is rated at 40W RF output for continuous carrier operation but under radar short pulse applications it is capable of 5kW peak power without exceeding the 100W anode dissipation. If the transmit pulse duration is 1μs and the time between adjacent transmit pulses is 1ms then the duty cycle is 0.01% and the valve is in the standby state for 99.99% of the time and has ample opportunity to dissipate the anode heat.

sions the duty cycle falls to between 30 to 50% and the average dissipation falls by a similar amount, so the average anode dissipation will be reduced to a safe level under this condition.

If the anode dissipation can be raised by an improved cooling system the valve can be safely pressed a little more without endangering it. A common method is to convert from air-cooling to a form of liquid cooling. Using a water-cooled anode can raise the anode dissipation by at least 100%, for the 2C39 series family up to 400% is practical with little effort.

Circuit losses

The anode efficiency is but one factor in determining the useful output power an RF amplifier can deliver for a given DC input. The matching network between the anode and the antenna also contains some loss and this can be significant at high frequency. Valve manufacturers often handle this by quoting two values for the output power in watts. They construct a test amplifier using the best quality components and use this to establish the output power under various operating conditions of anode voltage, anode current and drive power. One is known as 'useful output power' or 'load power' and is the RF power measured at the amplifier output terminal. This includes the losses in the anode-matching network. To establish the power exiting the anode they remove the valve from the test amplifier and then determine the loss between the anode and the amplifier output terminal. From this they can calculate the RF power exiting the anode, the 'available anode power'.

Suppose the anode network introduces 1dB of loss, this in round numbers is 20%. So if the amplifier develops 100W at the output the anode is developing 120W and 20W is dissipated as heat in the anode-matching network and is lost.

At HF and low VHF the circuit losses are quite small, but at UHF and microwaves the losses can be as high as 2dB, which is 40% in round numbers. Hence, the quality of the anode-matching network becomes more important as the operating frequency rises.

Calculation of component values

As an exercise, let us run through the steps to set up a typical triode valve as an audio amplifier. We will use a typical small signal type often used as a microphone amplifier and determine the values of the anode load resistor, cathode biasing resistor and the various capacitors to make a practical circuit.

We will choose a voltage supply of +250V DC and as we need to have good linearity (low distortion) we will choose Class-A operation. This means we need to set the quiescent anode voltage to 50% of the supply voltage and the anode current to 50% of its peak potential. This is shown in **Fig 12.6**.

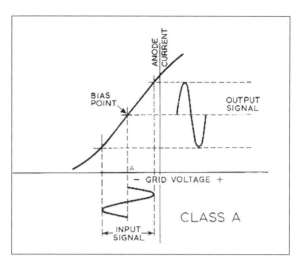

Note the shape of the anode current curve. At very low and very high anode current it deviates away from a straight line and this causes distortion. For best linearity we need to operate only on the straight-line portion of the curve.

Examining the manufacturer's data book for the chosen valve gives us some information to begin the calculations. The value of g_m is 2mA/V at an anode current of 3mA. Since we cannot swing the anode voltage below about 75% of the quiescent biasing point, or higher than 75% of the same point, this sets the maximum value for the anode load resistor. So we can now calculate the anode load resistor. We will choose a quiescent anode voltage of ≈50% of the supply voltage; this is +125V with respect to ground. So when a current of 3mA is flowing in the anode load resistor we need to drop 125V. Using Ohm's law we find R_A. Since R = V / I, V = 125V and I = 3mA, R_A = (125/ 0.003) = 41.66kΩ and a 39kΩ resistor is the nearest standard E12 value. (If we wanted to be pedantic two 82kΩ resistors connected in parallel would be a bit closer, or an E24 value of 43kΩ but this is not normally necessary).

Fig 12.6. Triode valve Class-A biasing

Now we need to establish the value of R_K to give the correct biasing. The manufacturer's data curves when examined gives a value of -2V for Vg1. Since the same 3mA is flowing in R_K and we need to establish +2V between the cathode and ground this requires a resistor of:

$$R_K = V_K / I_A = (2 / 0.003) = 666Ω$$

and could be obtained by two 330Ω resistors connected in series. The nearest E12 resistor is a 680Ω and normally will be close enough.

We now need to calculate the capacitor value that needs to be connected across R_K to eliminate audio voltage changes when the valve is driven by an input signal. The general rule of thumb is that the reactance of the capacitor needs to be at least 10 times less than the resistor value. Hence, we need to calculate the capacitor value that will be less than 68Ω at the lowest input frequency. For communications audio quality we can assume the lowest audio frequency will be about 300Hz, so this gives the parameters to calculate the value. This yields a value of 7.8μF and so a 10μF or greater value electrolytic would be suitable. If the amplifier were intended for hi-fi applications the capacitor would need to be a much larger value and 47μF would be suitable.

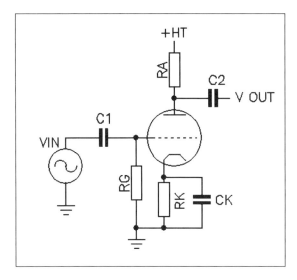

Fig 12.7. Basic triode amplifier

Having now correctly biased the valve to a quiescent current of 3mA we can determine the voltage gain. The voltage gain is given to a first approximation by $R_A \times g_m$. So with the 39kΩ anode load we expect a voltage gain of (39000 x 0.002) = 78. The basic amplifier is shown in **Fig 12.7** (which is Fig 12.3 repeated to save the trouble of turning back to the beginning of the chapter).

The output voltage swing will be determined by the input drive signal. As we have already seen, the valve will vary the anode current by 2mA for each volt change on the grid. Let us assume the input signal is a microphone with a maximum output voltage of 100mV rms. Hence, the anode voltage swing will be (78 x 0.1) = 7.8V rms into a high resistance load. We also need to convert the rms voltage to peak-peak to ensure we are not exceeding the linearity conditions. A 100mV rms signal is a peak-peak voltage of 0.2828V, so the anode voltage swing will be (7.8 x 2.828) = 22.05V p-p. This voltage swings symmetrically about the +125V bias point, about 11V either side. Since this is much smaller than the 125V at which the anode is biased to, the linearity should be excellent.

Effective valve resistance

What is probably not obvious from this is the value of the *valve resistance*. We have actually made a potential divider using the anode load resistor and the valve resistance to attain ≈50% of the supply voltage. We can now see that the valve is behaving like a 39kΩ resistor connected from the anode to ground. By varying the grid-input signal we are effectively varying the valve resistance. This is shown in **Fig 12.8**. RAK is the valve resistance between anode-cathode and RL is the anode load resistor. When the grid is driven more positive the anode current rises and RAK is now a lower value, hence the anode voltage (VA) falls towards ground. The opposite occurs when grid voltage is more negative, the anode draws less current and RAK increases in value and so the anode voltage rises towards the supply voltage.

Fig 12.8. Effective anode circuit

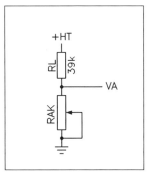

You may be wondering how much voltage swing we can achieve before the amplifier is driven into clipping? That is simple to calculate. If you remember we biased the valve to 3mA quiescent current and the conductance is 2mA/V, then if a 2V p-p input signal is applied the anode will swing between 1mA and 5mA. This is a total variation of 4mA and across a 39kΩ resistor it will develop (39 x 4) Volts which is 156V p-p, or 78V either side of +125V. Since the output voltage swings symmetrically about the quiescent voltage point of +125V it will swing down to (125 - 78) = +47V and up to

The minimum valve resistance is normally quoted in the data sheet, for a small signal amplifier the value can be quite high, often between 5kΩ and as high as 100kΩ. So although the valve may be fully turned on it still presents a fairly high resistance. For example, the ECC83 (12AX7) twin-triode used as a high gain audio preamplifier has a maximum resistance of 80kΩ when operated at 100V anode supply and 62.5kΩ when operated at 250V. For this reason it is only rated at 1.2mA anode current.

(125 + 78) = +203V. Because the valve needs at least 50V anode-cathode voltage to work in a linear manner this is about the limit of output voltage swing we can obtain. Note that the limitation is the anode load resistor and not the input signal swing. With the grid biased to -2V, with a 2V p-p input voltage swing the grid will swing between -1V and -3V. Since it remains above the 0V grid current point by 1V no grid current should flow.

If we reduce the anode load resistor in value the quiescent anode voltage (VA) will move towards the supply rail unless we change the cathode biasing resistor to increase the anode current to compensate. This would require a greater anode current and hence a lower grid voltage, more positive, and this sets the limit on how much anode voltage swing we can obtain because the grid voltage is closer to the grid current point.

If we increase the anode load resistor we then need to reduce the quiescent anode current to bring the anode voltage to half-rail. This requires a greater grid bias voltage and hence a larger value for R_K. This limits the usefulness of the simple triode amplifier and it is generally best to stay close to the manufacturer's recommended operating conditions to obtain the lowest distortion.

Capacitor values

The input and output capacitors need to be low reactance at the lowest operating frequency. Because the input and output are high impedance these can be quite low values, typically 100nF would suit most applications. The output capacitor needs to be rated for the anode voltage and a 250V capacitor would be the lowest voltage required. The input capacitor can be any convenient voltage because it only experiences a few volts, a 25V or 50V disc ceramic would be suitable.

Fixed grid bias

For circuits where the grid input signal may be high, a better option is to utilise a fixed grid bias method. This is often derived from a power supply and if made variable allows a better setting of the anode quiescent current. This is shown in **Fig 12.9**. The grid bias is fed via the resistor RG, which can be a lower value resistor. The cathode is now tied directly to ground eliminating the voltage drop of the cathode resistor and the cathode decoupling capacitor. If the grid bias is derived from a stiff supply (low impedance) then the application of input signal does not cause the grid bias voltage to change when grid current flows when the grid is driven positive.

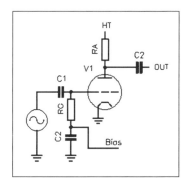

Fig 12.9. Fixed grid bias circuit

Operating classes: valve biasing

Disadvantage of Class-A

Whereas biasing to Class-A gives very low distortion the penalty paid is the high anode dissipation. Because the valve is biased to approx 50% of its rated peak anode current the efficiency is poor. The input signal is used throughout the whole 360°, so the linearity is very good. Class-A is normally only used where excellent linearity is a necessity and the power output is low. For higher power output levels we can change to another operating class known as Class-B.

Class-B

When Class-B is chosen the anode quiescent current is reduced to a low value, as little as 5% of the peak anode current when fully driven. This is obtained by increasing the grid bias voltage. The disadvantage of Class-B is that now we can only operate on one half cycle of the input waveform and the output waveform looks more like a rectifier with the opposite half cycle missing. This is shown in **Fig 12.10**.

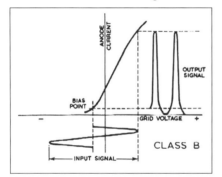

Because we are only using half the possible input waveform it is normally necessary to connect two valves in push-pull each of which operates on a half cycle and the outputs are then combined to give a complete sinusoidal waveform. Class-B can be successfully used as a RF amplifier when a resonant anode circuit is employed. The resonant circuit completes the missing half of the waveform and reasonably low distortion can be obtained.

The advantage of Class-B is that we are now using the whole of the linear portion of the anode transfer curve and hence the power output and efficiency are much higher than for Class-A operation.

Fig 12.10. Class-B biasing

Class-C

Class-C operation is normally used only for RF amplifiers where efficiency is critical and linearity is not a criterion, for example CW and FM transmitters. If we try and use a Class-C amplifier for SSB the distortion would be very high; hence it is not possible to use it for this mode. In Class-C the valve is biased to well beyond the cut-off point so that no anode current flows when the input signal is missing. This requires a much greater input signal swing than the other classes and hence more driving power. The anode current curve is shown in **Fig 12.11**.

Fig 12.11. Class-C operation

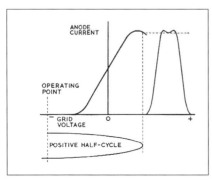

The anode current is driven into saturation and hence the output waveform is very distorted. Class-C amplifiers are used where we need to generate harmonics of the input signal, for example frequency multipliers. They also give high efficiency when a resonant anode network is used to couple the output power to the antenna. The resonant network filtering out the harmonics and filling in the missing half of the waveform.

Class-AB1

Where linearity is critical, for example when amplifying an SSB signal, we can choose a new point of operation which is somewhere between full Class-A and B. The first of these is known as AB1. The grid bias is adjusted so that a fairly high quiescent anode current flows with no drive signal, but not as high as for Class-A. This allows the full 360° of input waveform to be used and hence the linearity and efficiency are both good. A rule of thumb is to bias the valve such that the anode dissipation with no drive is approx two-thirds of the valve's rating. For example, the 4CX250B has an anode dissipation of 250W and if a 2000V DC anode supply is used and the quiescent current is 60mA the dissipation will be 120W. As this is less than the maximum it is a safe operating point.

Class-AB2

Class-AB2 is similar to AB1 except the grid bias voltage is higher and the quiescent anode current is more like true Class-B. This gives slightly better efficiency but slightly poorer linearity. Class-AB2 is popular for push-pull amplifiers because the inherent non-linearity in the two valves tends to cancel out and the harmonic content is less than a single ended amplifier.

Efficiency possible with different classes

The valve manufacturer Eimac gives values in its documentation of the efficiency possible for different operating classes. This is reproduced in **Fig 12.12**.

From this it will be seen that the more linear the class the lower the efficiency. Hence, an RF amplifier running in Class-AB1 may only attain about 50% efficiency. A Class-B amplifier attains a theoretical efficiency of 66% and Class-C theoretically runs as high as the high 90%. However, these are the theoretical figures and a practical valve RF amplifier can be expected to be at least 10 to 20% worse than these figures. Hence, a Class-AB1 linear amplifier may only attain an efficiency of 40% at best.

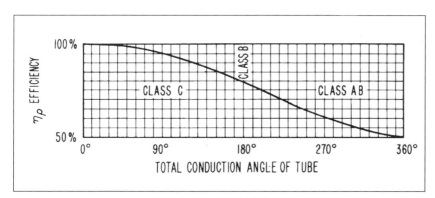

Fig 12.12. Efficiency versus class of operation (*courtesy of Eimac*)

Problems with capacitive coupled valve amplifiers

When two or more valves are connected in series to give more gain than a single stage can, coupling capacitors between the anode of the first valve and the grid of the next stage often perform this function. This is shown in **Fig 12.13**.

The anode of V1 has a 100nF capacitor C2 connecting to the grid of V2. The grid resistor of V2 is a high value resistor, typically 1MΩ. The anode of V1 is biased to half the supply rail, hence the voltage on one side of C2 is, say, +125V and the other side is at the grid potential of V2, say -10V. Hence, the voltage across C2 is 135V. The voltage rating of C2 needs to be chosen to be at least the high voltage supply rail, because the anode of V1 will swing up to close to this value. If C2 has a high leakage current, the grid bias of V2 will be overcome and the valve driven into a non-linear region. Even a few µA of leakage current is enough to disturb the biasing of V2. If 1µA of leakage current flows in C2 then the grid voltage of V2 will be raised by 1V if the grid resistor is 1MΩ. If the leakage current is 10µA, the grid of V2 will be driven to 0V with respect to the cathode.

This is a common problem with older equipment. The coupling capacitor dry out with age and heat and the leakage current becomes excessive; the grids are driven positive, causing distortion. Many of the older paper-foil coupling capacitors suffer from this problem with age. If the equipment has been out of service for several years the capacitors may develop a high leakage current. Probing a valve grid with a normal multi-meter set to DC volts often does not show the problem. This is because the resistance of the meter is often 20kΩ per volt and if the 3V range is selected this is only 60kΩ and is lower than the grid resistor and serves to shunt the leakage current to ground, so giving a false result. A better method is to attach the probe of a CRO or valve / FET or digital voltmeter across the grid to ground to measure the DC voltage present. These instruments have much

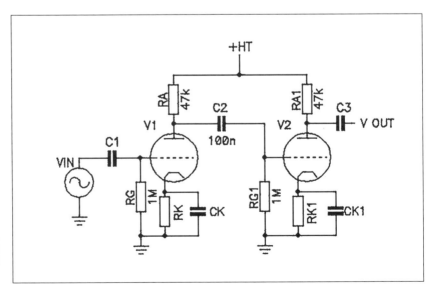

Fig 12.13. Capacitor coupling between stages

higher resistance than types such as a typical analog multi-meter.

The other common problem with old valve equipment is that the resistors tend to increase in value with age, especially if the resistor is dissipating a fair amount of power and tends to run hot. In older equipment the resistors are often carbon composition and these are renowned for increasing in value with age. Often anode and screen grid supply resistors can increase in value by as much as 50%. This changes the DC operating point and distortion occurs. Replacing these old carbon composition resistors with modern metal film or carbon film resistors is a much better option. If calculation show the resistor is dissipating say 0.5W, a 1W modern resistor will give long and reliable service.

Anode voltage waveforms for a RF amplifier

Unlike the resistive anode load used for Class-A audio amplifiers, the anode network used for RF amplifiers causes the anode voltage to swing above as well as below the nominal anode DC supply voltage. This is illustrated in **Fig 12.14**.

When the anode voltage is driven towards ground by a positive voltage on the grid, it reacts when the grid voltage is removed by flying upwards to a value of the same voltage excursion as when fully driven. This means the peak anode voltage at resonance is approximately twice the anode DC supply voltage. In practice the lower excursion will not reach all the way to ground, but to a point typically about 10% above ground. This is because the valve needs a certain minimum anode to cathode voltage to work correctly, the so-called anode-cathode saturation voltage. If the valve is a tetrode or pentode the anode voltage cannot safely swing lower than the screen voltage. You can think of this as a tension spring with one end attached to the ceiling and loaded with a weight such that the spring is extended to 50% of its full length. If we now pull down on the weight so that the spring is fully extended and then let go the weight will fly upwards by a similar amount and strike the ceiling. It will then oscillate around the mid-point when it falls down again.

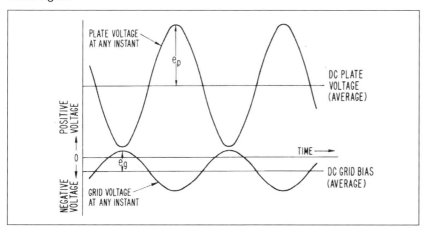

Fig 12.14. Anode voltage wave-form for a resonant anode network (*courtesy of Eimac*)

Valve pin out details

Pin	Function	
	EF95 / 6AK5:	**6C4 / EC90:**
1	Grid 1	Anode
2	Grid 3	No Connection (do not use)
3	Filament	Filament
4	Filament	Filament
5	Anode	Anode (internally connected to pin 1)
6	Grid 2	Grid 1
7	Cathode	Cathode
	Filament voltage 6.3V AC @ 0.15A	

12AU7, 12AT7 and 12AX7:

Pin	Function	
1	Anode	valve 1
2	Control Grid	valve 1
3	Cathode	valve 1
4	Filament 1	see notes
5	Filament 2	see notes
6	Anode	valve 2
7	Control Grid	valve 2
8	Cathode	valve 2
9	Filament	centre tap
	Filament voltage 12.6 or 6.3V AC @ 0.15A or 0.3A	

ECF82 / 6U8:

Pin	Function	
1	Anode	triode section
2	Control Grid	pentode section
3	Screen grid	pentode section
4	Filament 1	see notes
5	Filament 2	see notes
6	Anode	pentode section
7	Cathode	pentode section
8	Cathode	triode section
9	Control Grid	triode section
	Filament voltage 6.3V AC @ 0.45A	

Notes: Some of the valves shown in the circuits are types with a single filament designed only for 6.3V AC. To operate on 12.6V two valves with the same filament current can be connected in series. Valves such as the 12AT7 have either 12.6V filaments or they can be configured for 6.3V by paralleling the two filaments. Depending on the filament winding available on the transformer will determine the best option.

For those who are unfamiliar with the way the pins are identified, it is simple. Hold the valve so that the pins are facing you and rotate the valve until the gap between the pins is at 6 o'clock. See **Fig 12.15**. Counting around in a clockwise direction from the gap the first pin will be at about 7 o'clock and the pins are numbered 1, 2, 3 etc. The final pin will be at about 5 o'clock.

Fig 12.15. B9A base valve pins

British receiving valve numbering system

British receiving valves have a different numbering system to the American versions. Often one or the other part number is quoted and sometimes both for convenience. The following is the basis of the British numbering system. It is quite logical once you understand the system, but it does have a few quirks! It was originally defined by Mullard and continued by Philips. In later years the British Valve Association comprising the major British companies manufacturing valves adopted this system.

For example, a valve might have the part number EF91. The first letter denotes the filament voltage or current. E denotes a 6.3V filament and other valves used for television receivers used the letter P or U denoting a higher voltage, typically between 7 to 55V, but with a 300mA or 100mA current rating (P = 300mA, U = 100mA). This is because it was common to connect all the filaments in series across the 230V AC input with a common dropper resistor. Therefore all the valves needed to have the same filament current, or three 100mA valve filaments connected in parallel to achieve the same result when the other valves were 300mA types.

The second letter denotes the type of valve. This starts out being fairly logical but becomes difficult as time goes by and the logic seems to fall apart. As no valve can have fewer than two electrodes it is logical to start with the second letter in the alphabet, B. Hence a valve beginning with EB has a 6.3V filament and is a diode (in fact the letter B is used to denote a valve with a double diode). Continuing this logic a valve with EC would be a 6.3V filament and a triode.

If the valve contains more than one valve within the envelope the third letter describes this valve. For example an ECC81 is a 6.3V filament valve containing two triodes.

The next valve up would be a tetrode and we would expect that the fourth letter in the alphabet (D) was used for this, but we would be

173

wrong. The letter L denotes a tetrode or pentode intended for audio power output applications.

A pentode contains five electrodes and we would expect the fifth letter in the alphabet (E) or perhaps the letter P, but again we are wrong: it uses the letter F - but only if it is a small signal type.

The final valve is the heptode, which contains six electrodes and we might expect the sixth letter to be used (F), but this is already allocated to the pentodes, so once again we are wrong. It uses the letter H, which stands for heptode, which at least is logical.

We can list a few common valves and denote the types using these rules in **Table 12.1**. The equivalent American part is also given.

Table 12.1. Common valve types and their American equivalents

Designation		Description
British	American	
EB91	6AL5	6.3V filament valve containing two diodes
EBC80	6BD7	6.3V filament valve containing two diodes + triode
ECC81	12AT7*	6.3V filament valve containing two triodes
ECL82	6BM8	6.3V filament valve containing a triode and a tetrode
ECF82	6U8	6.3V filament valve containing a triode and a pentode
EF91	6AM6	6.3V filament valve containing a single pentode
ECH80	6AN7	6.3V filament valve containing a triode and a heptode

* Note: The ECC81 series is also known under the American part number of 12AT7, which means it has a 12V filament, but it can be strapped to operate on 6.3V.

There are a few oddities in the numbering system, like the EB91 mentioned above; another example is the E88CC. This is a special quality (SQ) version of the ECC88 intended for arduous duty, such as high vibration. Another one is the E180F, which is again a SQ version of the EF180.

The full British numbering system is shown in **Table 12.2** opposite, with the explanation. This was ratified by the British Valve Association (BVA). The letters after the filament details are in alphabetical order; for example EBCxx would be a 6.3V filament with a dual diode and one triode contained in the envelope.

Fig 12.16. Example of Loctal valve: a 5B/257M (miniature version of the 807)

174

1st letter	Filament details
A	4V type
B	0.18A (series connection)
C	0.2A (series connection)
D	1.4V (series or parallel connection)
E	6.3V (series or parallel connection)
F	12.6V
G	5V (parallel connection)
H	0.15A (series connection)
K	2V
L	0.45A (series connection)
P	0.3A (series connection)
U	0.1A (series connection)
V	0.05A (series connection)
X	0.6A (series connection)
Y	0.45A (series connection)

2nd/3rd letter	Construction
A	Single diode (excluding rectifiers)
B	Double diode
C	Triode, small signal types
D	Triode, power output types (e.g. television receiver shunt stabiliser types)
E	Tetrode, small signal types
F	Pentode, small signal types
L	Tetrode or pentode, power output types, including television receiver types
H	Hexode or Heptode
K	Octode or Heptode
M	'Magic eye' tuning indicator types
N	Gas filled triode or thyratron
Q	Nonode
X	Full wave rectifier or double diode (gas filled)
Y	Half wave rectifier types (vacuum)
Z	Full wave rectifier types (vacuum)

1st digit	Basing details
1-10	Miscellaneous types (side contact)
11-21	Miscellaneous types (footless)
21-30	Loctal (8-pin glass base)
31-39	International Octal (8-pin paxolin base) also 300 series
40-49	8-pin (miniature) B8A also 141-149 series
60 & 70	Sub miniature types
80-89	B9A glass base also 180 & 800 series
90-99	Miniature (B7G glass base)
200 series	B10D base
500 series	B9D series

Remaining digits: Signal pentodes and tetrodes that end in even numbers are sharp cut off valves. Those ending in odd numbers are remote cut off valves. For operation as a mixer a sharp cut off valve is required, for AGC control a remote cut off valve is required.

Table 12.2. British valve numbering system as ratified by the BVA

CV Numbers: Format is CV followed by up to five digits, e.g. CV4004. The CV numbering system is used by the British military to denote valves, transistors etc.

CV numbers can be converted into a NATO stock number (NSN). For example, 5960-xx-000-yyyy. The xx denotes the country of manufacture where the UK is designated as 99. A NSN of 5960-99-000-4004 is a CV4004 made in the UK. Valve screening cans have the NSN format of 5960-xx-056-yyyy. For example 5960-99-056-3003 is a short B7G screening can made in the UK and 5960-99-056-3005 is the taller version. A standard height B9A screening can is 5960-xx-056-3007 and 5960-xx-056-3009 is the taller version.

CHAPTER 13

Circuits using valves

In this chapter:

- Experimental valve receiver
- Mixer
- Local oscillator
- RF amplifier
- Product detector for SSB and CW
- S-meter circuit
- Constructing using valves: modern techniques
- Low noise RF amplifier
- High voltage stabilised supply
- Simple economy high voltage supply
- Types of valves for RF amplifiers

V ALVES ARE a very good option for receivers, even though many amateurs regard them as old fashioned. The benefits of using valves are the superior signal handling and the ease of applying AGC. A simple HF receiver allowing AM, CW and SSB reception could use as few as five valves and offer good sensitivity and signal handling characteristics to strong signals.

A well-constructed valve receiver can often outperform a modern solid-state version by a considerable margin under crowded band conditions. Many of the older valve receivers, although they may not be as sensitive as the modern varieties, have very good strong signal performance, often as much as 30dB better than a modern variety.

Experimental valve receiver

To demonstrate the various circuits, I made a single conversion receiver from 10.7MHz to 455kHz as the 'back end' of a receiving system for VHF. The front end consists of solid-state down converters with an IF of 10.7MHz with 50Ω output impedance.

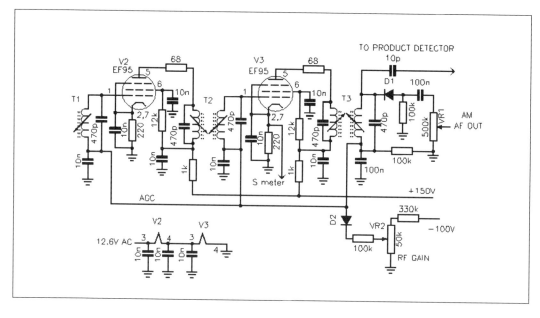

Fig 13.1. Simple AM IF amplifier

A simple AM IF amplifier is shown in **Fig 13.1**. This uses two small valves with B7G bases. The AGC and AM detector uses a silicon diode such as a 1N4148, although a lower forward drop diode like a Schottky (BAT-85) would give better results. Inter-stage coupling is using ready wound IF transformers. When correctly aligned, the IF bandwidth would be approx 6kHz which suits AM reception. All resistors are 0.5W rating and the capacitors need to be rated at 250V for the high voltage parts.

The valve chosen is the EF95 / 6AK5 / M8100, which is a high gain pentode with a remote 'cut-off' characteristic for optimum AGC control. Other suitable valves would be EF91 / 6AM6 or EF183, E180F, the latter two being in the B9A base. Two valves using an IF of 455kHz can be expected to give a gain of ≈70dB with excellent AGC control. IF transformers T1, T2 and T3 are ready wound types but could be substituted by home wound coils on formers with ferrite slugs. If ready wound transformers are used the tuning capacitors are normally built in and will not be required.

Note that the EF95 has two cathode pins and each must be decoupled with a 10nF ceramic disc capacitor for total stability. The cathode resistor can be attached to either cathode pin. The anode stopper resistors are normally necessary to preserve stability in this high gain amplifier. The IF transformers should be situated as close to the valves as possible to minimise the lead lengths and reduce RF radiation from the leads. Although only operating at 455kHz the two stages have a potential gain of almost 80dB and can be unstable if the layout is not optimal. Grounding should be by very short leads to the chassis.

The detector diode D1 rectifies the RF signal to produce an audio signal and also generates the negative AGC voltage for the control grids of the IF amplifier valves. The AGC attack and decay times are determined by the 100nF capacitor and the 100kΩ discharge resistor. The audio output can be fed to another suitable valve as a loudspeaker driver, or a modern IC could be used. VR1 is the volume control and should be a log-law type. If manual RF gain control is required, a negative voltage from a supply and adjusted by a linear potentiometer can be used to bias the valves nearer to cut off and fed into the AGC line by a diode (D2). (An alternative method would be to lift the two 220Ω cathode resistors from ground and connect them together to a variable resistor of about 5kΩ that then varies the cathode bias voltage. This method is not as good as the negative bias supplied via a preset pot shown in the diagram and will lead to higher distortion when a strong signal is received).

An important thing to note is the decoupling of the heater pins on all valves. Because of the high gain involved spurious signals can be conducted along the heater wires from one stage to another. Until the heater pins were properly decoupled instability was observed at some signal levels. Another important consideration is the high impedance signal from the anode of the final IF amplifier that can radiate and this could then be picked up by the first stage grid circuit causing instability (howl round). The signal feeding the product detector should be run in a shielded cable to prevent radiation. When an input signal of 10mV at the antenna is applied the RF voltage at the anode of the final IF amplifier anode is approx 10V p-p and this can radiate into other stages.

Mixer

The first IF transformer (T1) connects to the mixer stage, only the secondary is shown in Fig 12.15. The mixer stage is shown in **Fig 13.2**. A suitable valve is the ECF82 / 6U8 which contains a triode and a pentode in one envelope, the triode could be used for the LO stage or as a grounded grid RF amplifier. The filament of the 6U8 is 6.3V @ 0.45A so will require a 6.3V AC winding on the transformer or a suitable dropper resistor (15Ω / 5W) from a 12.6V AC supply.

The primary of T1 selects the desired IF and this is further amplified by the IF amplifier shown in Fig 13.1. No AGC is applied to the mixer stage to prevent pulling of the local oscillator. The conversion gain of the mixer is approx 12dB. On the higher bands a 'grid-stopper' resistor may be required in series with the control grid and / or anode to preserve stability, a value of 22Ω to 100Ω is normally adequate. The LO signal is injected onto the cathode of the pentode via a coupling capacitor. The required LO amplitude is approx 5V rms for best mixing efficiency. This can be either a fixed frequency oscillator provided by a crystal oscillator or a variable frequency oscillator derived from a VFO circuit. Note that in the ECF82 / 6U8 the suppressor grid (grid-3) is internally connected to the cathode (pin 7).

Fig 13.2. Mixer section

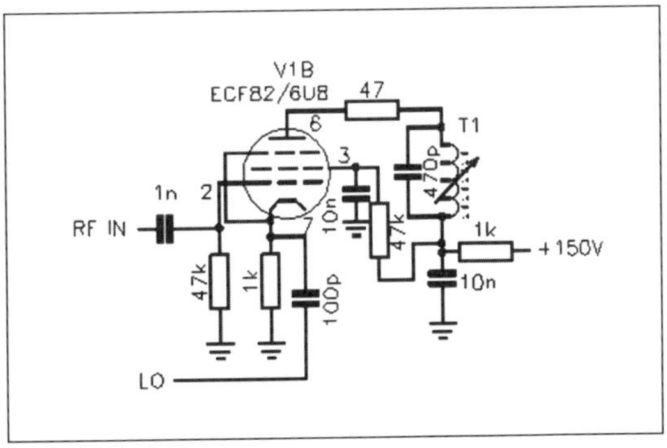

179

Local oscillator

A fixed LO is shown in **Fig 13.3** using a triode and a crystal configured as a Pierce oscillator. The triode is a 6C4 / EC90 although many other triodes are suitable. One half of a 12AT7, 12AU7 or E88CC would also be suitable. The crystal is adjusted on to the correct frequency by the parallel trimmer capacitor. The output from the anode is connected to the cathode of the mixer via a coupling capacitor. For best frequency stability the anode supply should be derived from a regulated supply. An OA2 gas stabiliser or a 150V / 1W zener diode can be used to feed the oscillator with a suitable dropper resistor from a higher supply voltage.

In my receiver the crystal was 10.245MHz to convert from 10.7MHz to 455kHz, the alternative crystal is 11.155MHz.

Fig 13.3. Crystal oscillator circuit

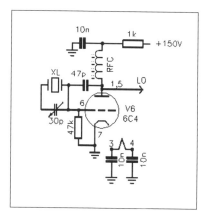

The oscillator injection needs to be at least 5V rms for best efficiency. With the circuit shown up to 10V rms is possible with a +150V supply voltage. If the output voltage is too high, the coupling capacitor value can be reduced to obtain the correct injection voltage or the value of the anode dropper resistor can be increased to lower the output power. (The LO power level with 5V rms is approx 25mW and this is why the mixer has a superior dynamic range compared to solid-state mixers using only a few mW of LO injection).

For best frequency stability when a VFO is used we can use a solid-state oscillator using junctions FETs and then feed the output into a triode amplifier to generate the required LO voltage. An output voltage of 0.5V rms from the VFO when fed into a triode amplifier will develop several volts for the LO.

RF amplifier

An amplifier stage to improve the sensitivity is shown in **Fig 13.4**. A dual triode such as the 12AT7 is rated up to 300MHz and at HF can generate about 20dB per stage with excellent strong signal handling. In my receiver the triode portion of the ECF82 / 6U8 was used, as the sensitivity required is not that high. (The sensitivity achieved was approx 10μV for 6dB S/N ratio using a CW carrier as the input signal).

Fig 13.4. Grounded grid RF amplifier

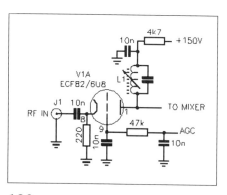

The antenna input is fed into the cathode of the first stage operating as a grounded grid amplifier. This presents an impedance close to 50Ω over a wide bandwidth. Attempting to operate as a grounded cathode stage will almost certainly lead to instability because of the high feedback capacitance from the anode to grid inherent in triodes. (If a grounded cathode amplifier is required a better option is a tetrode or pentode that inherently has a lower anode to grid feedback capacity). Operated as a grounded grid stage gives less gain but eliminates one tuned circuit for the grid circuit. A wide-band gain of about 13dB is possible at HF with the circuit shown. Keeping the RF gain low before the mixer improves the strong signal handling performance of a receiver.

The anode has a tuned circuit resonated to the operating frequency and coupled to the grid of the mixer stage by a capacitor. The tuned circuits are selected to suit the operating frequency. If instability is encountered a 'stopper resistor' of about 33Ω to 100Ω may be required between the tuned circuits and the anode. As with all high gain RF amplifiers component lead lengths, decoupling, shielding and construction play a large part in achieving a stable design. Decoupling capacitors should have minimum lead lengths and be a type suitable for the operating frequency.

If a pentode is used as an RF amplifier with a high Q tuned circuit in the grid and the anode, shielding will be required to prevent RF energy at the anode 'hopping over' into the grid circuit. If the shielding is insufficient the amplifier may turn into an oscillator!

Product detector for SSB and CW

To demodulate SSB and CW transmissions we need a different type of demodulator. This is commonly known as a product detector and the IF signal and a fixed carrier, the Beat Frequency Oscillator (BFO), are mixed together to obtain the audible difference frequency. The simplest product detector uses a twin-triode with the IF signal applied to one control grid and the beat frequency oscillator to the second cathode.

The basis of the circuit is shown in **Fig 13.5**. The twin-triode is a 12AT7 or E88CC with one half used as the carrier oscillator and the cathodes connected together with a small value coupling capacitor, the second half operating as a mixer stage. The IF signal is tapped off from the final IF transformer secondary at a high impedance and coupled into the control grid of the second triode, V4a.

The resulting audio signal will require further filtering to remove the RF signals also existing at the anode at pin 6. At the anode of V4a (pin 6)

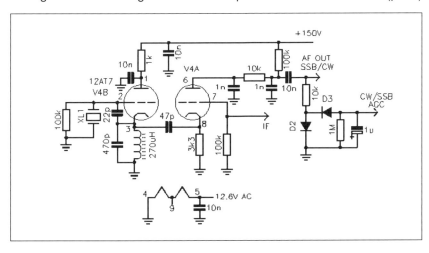

Fig 13.5. Product detector circuit

is a composite signal of the BFO plus the IF (≈910kHz) and the difference frequency that is the required audio beat note. A simple R-C low pass filter as shown is normally adequate.

Switching between AM and CW / SSB can be achieved by switching off the product detector oscillator anode supply when AM reception is required. Alternatively lifting the cathode of the oscillator half from ground will serve the same purpose to disable the detector.

For best SSB reception a narrow IF filter is required and a commercial 'block filter' inserted between the output of the mixer and the IF amplifier is the best option. This filter should have a bandwidth of about 2.5kHz.

The AGC system used for AM could be used for CW / SSB, although not optimal. When used in conjunction with some manual gain reduction by the RF gain control, mentioned earlier, it will be adequate. The AGC detector shown uses the audio envelope generated and has a fast attack and a slow decay to suit SSB signals.

The diodes are low forward voltage types, the BAT-85 Schottky diode is a good candidate for this application as today germanium diodes which were originally used are difficult to find.

When receiving AM the carrier oscillator is switched off. If the carrier oscillator is left running, carrier leakage from the oscillator will cause the AM IF amplifier to produce an AGC voltage which will limit the sensitivity. The audio from the AM and SSB detectors are switched to the audio amplifier stage. For SSB detection the carrier oscillator needs to be approx 1.5kHz lower or higher than the IF centre frequency. A 453.5kHz or 456.5kHz crystal is normally used. The crystal needs to be accurately tuned to the wanted frequency by a capacitor trimmer across the crystal.

For simple receivers the crystal can be replaced with an L-C tank circuit forming a BFO that can be adjusted over a small range. For SSB reception the oscillator needs to be adjusted so that it occurs in the correct place for demodulation; a small value variable capacitor across the inductor as well as a larger capacitor to set the centre frequency can be used to achieve this. For best stability the oscillator should be supplied by a stable supply voltage from a regulated supply, such as +100V from a zener diode.

S-meter circuit

A simple S-meter circuit is shown in **Fig 13.6**. The 1mA meter is connected between the cathode of the last IF amplifier valve and a potential divider. When the signal level increases the AGC voltage developed becomes more negative, so biasing the amplifier stages more towards cut off. As the cathode current decreases the meter indicates a higher current under these conditions.

VR2 is the 'set zero' control for zero signal condition. VR3 is the sensitivity adjustment. To set up the S-meter, discon-

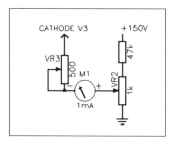

Fig 13.6. S-meter circuit

nect the antenna and connect a 50Ω load to the receiver input, then set VR2 to indicate zero on the meter. Inject a 50µV RF signal and adjust the sensitivity control for an indication of S9. With the simple receiver line up shown there are four stages connected in series with AGC applied to three stages. The total AGC range will be approx 100dB, giving excellent performance for weak or very strong signals.

Constructing using valves: modern techniques

Traditionally valve equipment was built upon a metal chassis normally made from aluminium or cadmium plated steel sheet folded up into a rectangular section. The holes for the valve bases were punched out using a set of chassis punches (Q-max™ etc) and other holes drilled for attaching tag strips, grounding solder tags or controls.

Often when following a published design the chassis would be drawn full size and the various holes etc dimensioned on the drawing. In some magazines the chassis drawing was a pull-out sheet that could be glued or taped on to a standard aluminium chassis and the hole centres marked with a centre punch using the paper as a guide.

For those lacking the necessary metal working skills or facilities to fold up and then punch and drill the numerous holes, sometimes a company would supply a prepared chassis which could be assembled and wired. Several famous amateur designs, such as the G2DAF receiver and transmitter, were available as sets of metalwork and major components from several mail order companies and many amateurs built a 'kit version'. Some of the older RSGB and ARRL handbooks contain several pages of advertisements near the back of companies (which no longer exist) for several of the popular designs of the day. One such company was E J Philpotts Metalworks Ltd who advertised the G2DAF communications receiver metalwork in the *RSGB Handbook* of 1964. In the same book is an advert for

Fig 13.7. A selection of auger bits and hole saws

Electroniques who listed the complete coil pack (32 coils and RF chokes), three-gang variable tuning capacitor and other variable capacitors, 19 switches and nine-piece IF transformer kit for the G2DAF receiver for the total sum of 15 guineas, or all parts were sold separately.

I favour a different technique using readily available material that allows a 'breadboard' version to be built for experimental purposes. One of the most difficult items is the many

grounding points required. In a normal chassis a hole would need to be drilled, deburred and then a solder tag with a screw, washer and nut fastened to the chassis. Often when an experimental design is being evolved only a vague circuit is available and it inevitably changes as the design develops. Having to drill and deburr the hole before fastening a solder tag to serve as a grounding point slows down the design and often leaves many holes which no longer serve a purpose. It can also cause problems with swarf and wires close by that can get tangled up in the drill bit if care is not taken.

Fig 13.8. A drilled piece of printed circuit board ready for construction

My 'breadboard chassis' is a piece of double-sided glass fibre printed circuit board 1.5mm thick. Often a suitable off cut can be scrounged from the scrap bin of a printed circuit board manufacturer and pressed into serv-

ice. The positions of the valve bases and other major components are marked out and the large holes can be cut using wood auger bits. These are flat two faced cutters that are available in many different sizes in 1mm increments. For B7G valve bases a 16mm bit is required (5/8in) and for the B9A valve bases a 19mm bit (3/4in). Using a pillar-drilling machine a pilot hole of about 4mm is drilled in the centre of the hole and the pointed centre of the wood auger bit uses this to guide the drill. Using a fairly slow speed, not more than 300RPM and steady pressure a clean round hole can be cut in a few seconds, requiring very little de-

burring. The printed circuit board is backed up by a piece of chipboard or softwood on the drilling machine table. An alternative to wood auger bits is a hole saw, but these tend to leave a ragged hole.

Fig 13.9. Top view of the experimental valve receiver

When the valve base holes have been cut, the fixing screws for the bases can be marked off using the bases as a guide and then drilled with a 3.2mm (1/8in) drill and 6BA or M3 screws and nuts used to attach the

bases to the 'chassis'. Grounding points are made by soldering directly to the copper clad board either on top or on the bottom. This allows components to be connected with minimal lead lengths between the valve base pins and ground.

Before drilling the valve base fixing holes establish the correct orientation of the pins to connect to other items. When all the holes have been drilled and deburred the board surfaces are cleaned with steel wool or some household scouring powder. When the board is spotlessly clean the board is

Fig 13.10. Experimental valve receiver breadboard underside

washed and dried either in the sun or using a hair dryer.

The breadboard is raised above the workbench by long hexagonal spacers fastened at the corners. This prevents damage to the components under the board. Screening panels can be cut from more glass fibre printed circuit board or thin tin plate or brass shim stock which are soldered into place. Other strips of board material can be soldered to the edges at right angles to form a box on which switches or other controls can be mounted.

One source of components is the many redundant pieces of surplus items that contain valve bases and IF transformers etc. These can be picked up at mobile rallies for next to nothing. I bought a car boot full of these recently for very little money and they proved to contain many useful and hard to find components. One item was a marine SSB HF transceiver that had been pensioned off. Although some of the valves were more than 60 years old they worked perfectly.

The small resistors and capacitors are often not worth rescuing because they will be aged and new modern types should be used when constructing an item. Avoid using the old Hunts capacitors (known as 'toffee types' because they have a chocolate brown outer coating) as they are known to leak badly when old. Valve screening cans, bases and coil formers in these surplus items are often of very high quality, often ceramic or PTFE bases or formers that work well up to UHF. Although the item may be beyond repair, the components they contain can be carefully removed and used for other projects. The marine HF transceiver contained three high quality crystal ovens each holding two HC-6/U crystals.

Fig 13.10 shows the underside of my experimental valve receiver breadboard. The various sections are screened with tin plated steel partitions and these have 1nF/300V feed through capacitors to carry the supply and signals between sections. These serve as tie points for many of the components. The product detector is in the left-hand bottom portion and the second IF amplifier is contained in the right hand portion. Top right is the first IF amplifier and the local oscillator and mixer is top left.

Low noise RF amplifier

To improve the sensitivity we can add an extra RF amplifier ahead of the mixer input. A high gain stage using a pentode is shown in **Fig 13.11**. This uses a 6AM6 / EF91 although many other valves are suitable, such as EF95, 6BZ6, 6BA6, 6BH6 and EF180. If the valve type is changed the pin connections may be different and should be checked.

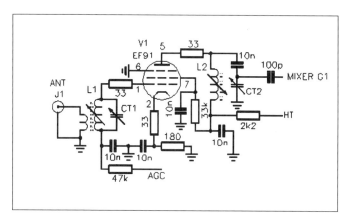

The antenna input is applied to L1 with a coupling winding of a few turns wound over the main winding. L1 is resonated with CT1, which is half of a dual-gang air variable capacitor. The second half (CT2) is used for the anode-tuned circuit. The value of L1, L2 and CT1, CT2 will depend on the operating frequency. The high gain means that the two tuned circuits must be adequately screened from each other to prevent instability. Often a tin plate shield positioned across the valve base will be adequate. Decoupling capacitors need to be suitable for RF operation and with minimal lead lengths. Normally 10nF ceramic disc capacitors can be used up to about 30MHz, for higher frequency operation a 4.7nF may be a better choice.

Methods used to improve the stability are the grid and anode stopper resistors and a partially decoupled cathode resistor, which applies some negative feedback. The output can be taken off the anode with a low value coupling capacitor as shown or by a link winding similar to the input tuned circuit.

For HF there is no need to strive for any more gain than about 20dB or a lower noise figure. (If used with the experimental receiver shown earlier the sensitivity will be approx 0.5µV, which is more than adequate even for 28MHz).

For VHF or UHF operation a grounded grid triode amplifier is normally necessary to preserve stability with high gain RF amplifiers. Triodes inherently have lower noise figures than multi-grid valves and will offer better performance above about 30MHz. Two cascaded grounded-grid triode stages at 50MHz can achieve in excess of 30dB of stable gain when correctly constructed and adjusted.

Fig 13.11. RF amplifier using EF91 pentode

High voltage stabilised supply

A basic series regulator to provide 300V with high stability is shown in **Fig 13.12**. The regulator can provide up to 150mA when fed from a nominal +450V raw DC supply. The series regulator uses a tetrode

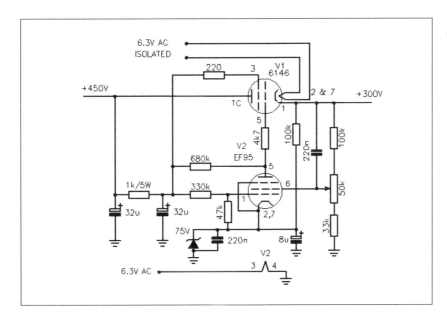

Fig 13.12. High voltage stabilised supply

or pentode; here the 6146 valve is shown as this is designed for this service as well as being used for RF power amplifier duty. An alternative is the 6L6. The control valve is the EF95 / 6AK5 as the current required is low. (The circuit shown was used in the Marconi Instruments TF1066 series of signal generators to supply the oscillator valve and the other low power stages. Originally the voltage reference was obtained from an 85V gas filled stabiliser valve but a zener diode is a better option today. The original regulator valve is no longer available and the 6146 valve is a good replacement).

All resistors are 0.5W types except the 1kΩ, which is a 5W wire-wound type, and the 100kΩ feeding the zener reference diode which should be a 1W. The supply requires two 6.3V AC heater windings on the transformer. The heater winding feeding the 6146 must be floating above ground due to the high voltage on the cathode. The heater winding for the EF95 can be grounded at one side if required, as the cathode voltage on this valve is only 75V. The 75V zener can be a 1W type. The 220nF capacitor needs to be rated at least 300V DC. Other output voltages can be obtained by scaling the output potential divider. When the desired voltage is set the pot slider will be at approx +75V. Output ripple voltage is less than 5mV rms at full load.

Simple economy high voltage supply

A simple multiple output power supply for low power valve equipment such as receivers is shown in **Fig 13.13**. The output voltages and current will depend on the transformer used. The transformer

Fig 13.13.
Simple economy
power supply

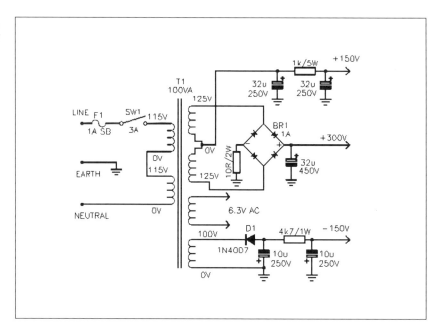

needs to wound with the required filament voltages required, either 6.3V or 12.6V AC can be obtained with two 6.3V windings connected in series or parallel. Only one filament winding is shown in the diagram. The smoothing capacitors need to be adequately rated for the off load voltages; the values shown are a good guide. The main high voltage rectifier can be a packaged bridge or made up from four diodes such as 1N4007. The choice of primary voltage will depend on the local supply voltage, the diagram shows two 115V primaries connected in series to suit a 230V AC supply (if the local supply is 115V the primaries are connected in parallel observing the correct phasing of the windings).

The main high voltage secondary is a centre tapped type and this feeds a bridge rectifier. The centre tap of the secondary provides an output voltage that is half the main high voltage output and this can supply approx 40% of the current that the main output supplies. The bridge rectifier has a low value resistor in series with the negative terminal; this acts as a fuse under a shorted output condition and will cause the resistor to heat up and blow open circuit.

For a receiver the 150V output can be used for the majority of the RF and IF amplifier stages as a voltage much in excess of 200V is of no benefit. The 300V output will power a 10W audio output amplifier with current to spare. For a low power transmitter the supply can supply a 30W output transmitter.

Ensure that the fusing and wiring is carried out with care. Although the highest voltage is only 300V this is enough to cause a nasty electric shock, and possibly a cardiac arrest, so extreme care needs to be exercised when testing the supply.

Types of valves for RF amplifiers

Finally on the subject of valves, a quick look at some of the valves used in RF power amplifiers (PAs). Many of the traditional valves used by amateurs were designed long before the days of SSB and hence are not specified for this type of duty. The 813 valve was originally released by RCA in 1938 and was intended only for Class-B audio applications or Class-C operation as RF amplifiers for CW and anode modulated AM transmitters. Valves such as the 6146 (QV06-20), although commonly used for SSB amplifiers, were not originally specified for this in the manufacturers' data sheets.

Only with the introduction of the 6146B in 1964 is any mention made of operation in linear Class-AB1, when SSB was well established. In the earlier data sheets of the 6146 and 6146A valves mention is only made of Class-C FM telephony duty and audio amplifiers using Class-AB1.

A popular driver valve for the 6146 is the 12BY7A pentode, but in the manufacturer's data sheet it is primarily intended as a television video output amplifier (this from a General Electric data sheet of 1955). No mention is made of its operation for RF amplifiers. (The oft-maligned 6JSC6, intended as a television receiver sweep tube, used by many Japanese manufacturers in the early days, has an anode dissipation of 30W, whereas the often-preferred 6146 only has 20W anode dissipation).

Another popular driver valve was the 6BW6 made amongst others by Brimar in the UK (Standard Telephones and Cables Limited). The data sheet from 1960 specifies operation primarily as a RF amplifier up to 150MHz and that it is identical in characteristics to the earlier 6V6GT valve and the commercial version of the CV2136 used in military equipment. The 6V6GT is a larger valve, approximately the same size as a 6146 and extensively used during WWII for VHF and radar applications.

The popular 5763 valve (QV03-12) that is often quoted as a beam tetrode is in fact a pentode (a lot of the amateur valve tables get this incorrect). It was released by RCA in May 1949 as shown by the data sheet, being marked 'tentative'. It was designated for oscillator and Class-C RF amplifier service using FM telephony only. Its useful operating frequency range is up to 175MHz and is detailed as a frequency doubler or tripler for high-band VHF transmitters as well as an output valve with 7W output power. It quickly became a useful valve for HF and VHF transmitters as well as being used in power supplies as a series regulator valve for stabilised high voltage supplies, something the 6146 is also used for extensively.

By contrast, valves such as the 3-500Z triode were designed primarily for SSB operation and this is confirmed in the original Eimac (Varian) data sheet from the period (March 1968). The first application page is headed by operation as a Class-B zero biased with IMD figures quoted for typical operation using SSB.

Although a valve may not be specifically rated for linear RF amplifier operation very often it can be used if the characteristics are studied carefully. A typical example is the 6JS6C used in many Japanese HF transmitters as output valves. These were originally intended for use as television receiver horizontal deflection (line output) amplifiers; Americans call these 'sweep tubes'. Another popular valve is the PL-504 for the same application with an unusual heater voltage of 27V because the filaments were connected in series across the 230V AC input. By comparison the popular EL84 is a similar pentode with a 6W maximum output rating, but with a 6.3V filament voltage. Although specified as an audio output stage device it can work satisfactorily up to about 7MHz at reduced ratings.

Appendix

- Pin out details

THE PIN out details of the devices used in the various circuits are shown below. In many circuits substitutions may be made with little change in performance. If a substitution is made it would be prudent to check with the manufacturer for the correct pin out data!

Note: Pins marked NC mean 'no connection' and this pin can be left floating or tied to ground.

Small signal transistors

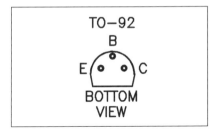

Many TO-92 transistors are supplied with the pins in a straight line. Some are preformed to the TO-18 standard and others are preformed to a reverse TO-18 format so care needs to be exercised before soldering into circuit!

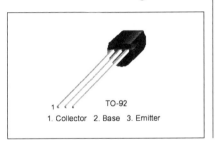
1. Collector 2. Base 3. Emitter

An exception to the normal connection is the MPSH-10 and J310 RF transistors, which have the pin out shown below.

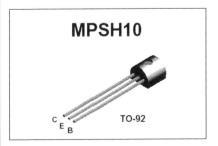

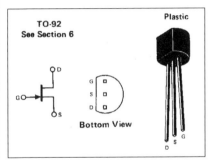

Note: Many small signal JFET devices drain and source pins are interchangeable: they can be connected either way in the circuit with little difference in performance.

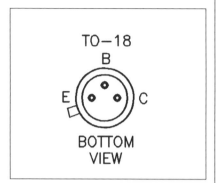

Metal can TO-18 format, now becoming obsolete. The tab on the can identifies the emitter. NPN and PNP types both have the same pin out so care needs to be taken when using these types. The metal can is internally connected to the collector.

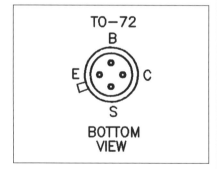

Metal can TO-72 used for small signal RF transistors, e.g. BFY90. Now almost obsolete. The S pin is the screen, which is connected to the metal can. Some early dual gate mosfets (e.g. 3N201, 40673) used the same can. The can in these is connected to the Source.

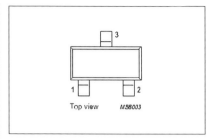

Surface Mount transistors (SOT23). Most small signal transistors use the following pin out: Pin 1 = base, pin 2 = emitter, pin 3 = collector. Some versions use reverse pinning for the base and emitter, these are suffixed with an R in the part number e.g. BFR92AR.

RF small signal transistors

All dual gate mosfets use the same pin out whether a conventional package or an SMD type. The pins looking from above are counted clockwise from the Drain pin in the order: Drain, Source, Gate-1, Gate-2. However, SMD types may be supplied with reverse pinning - see comments below. The correct mounting is with the writing on the case facing up.

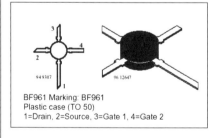

BF961 Marking: BF961
Plastic case (TO 50)
1=Drain, 2=Source, 3=Gate 1, 4=Gate 2

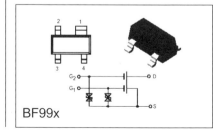

BF99x

For the SMD version the wide pin is the Source (pin 1).
Source = 1, Drain = 2, Gate-2 = 3
Gate-1 = 4.
Note: A device with R as the last part of the type number (e.g. BF996R) has reversed pinning for the gates and drain and source. However, the wide pin is always the Source!

Large signal transistors

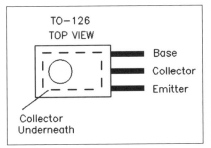

TO-126 package
Most medium power bipolar transistors use this pin out. Note the base and emitter pin out is different to the TO-220 versions!

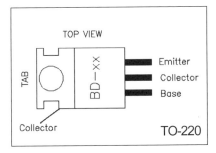

TO-220 package
Most bipolar transistors use this pinout. Thyristors (SCR) pin out is normally Cathode = Base, Anode = Collector, Gate = Emitter. The anode is internally connected to the tab.

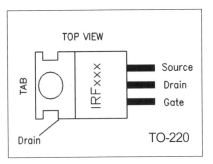

Most switching mosfets use this pin out. The drain is internally connected to the tab.

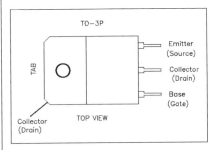

TO-3P / TO-247
Used by higher power bipolar transistors e.g. TIP-140 series and some high power mosfets.

Integrated Circuits

Voltage regulators

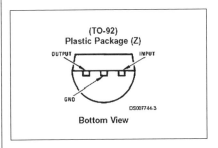

TO-92
Typical 100mA regulators use this pin out, e.g. LM78Lxx.

Negative voltage regulators, e.g. LM79Lxx, series use the pin out below

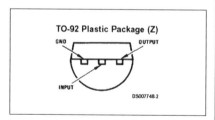

100mA negative voltage regulator.

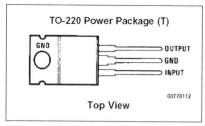

Most three terminal positive voltage regulators use this pin out. The tab is connected to the ground pin internally. Negative voltage regulators use a different pin out shown below.

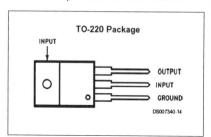

Negative voltage regulator.

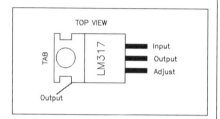

LM-317 adjustable regulator. Note: The tab is connected to the Vout pin.

Switching regulators

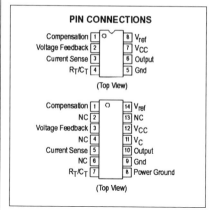

UC384x series pin out.

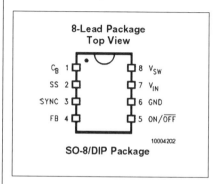

LM2671 Switching Regulator

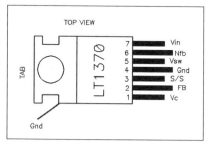

LT1370 Switching Regulator

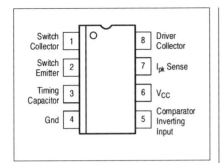

MC34063 Low Power Switch mode IC

Operational Amplifiers and comparators

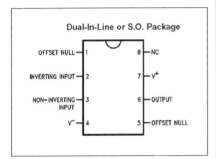

LM741, NE5534 & CA3140 Single Op-Amp

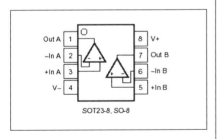

NE5532, LM358 and CA3240 Dual Op-Amp

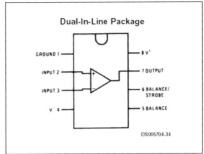

LM311 series single Comparator

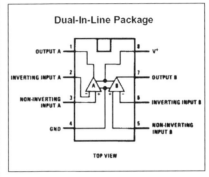

LM393 series dual comparators

Special Integrated Circuits

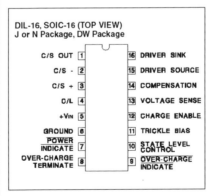

UC2906 Ni-Cd Charger IC

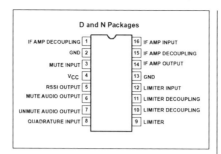

NE604/614/624 IF amplifier IC

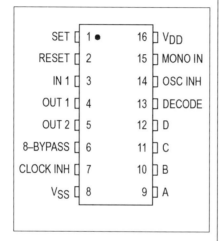

MC14536 Timer IC

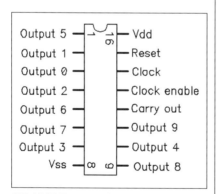

CD4017 Decade Counter

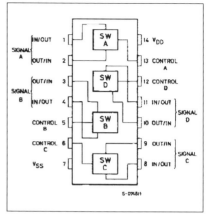

CD4066 Quad Analog Switch

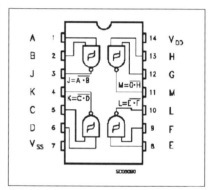

CD4093 Quad Nand gate

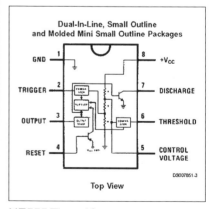

NE555 Timer IC

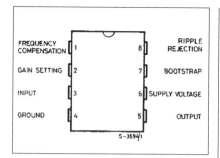

TBA820M Low Power AF Amplifier

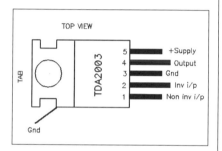

TDA2003 High Power AF Amplifier

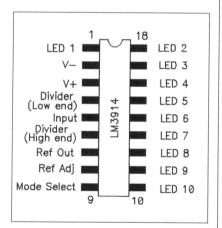

LM3914 LED Driver IC

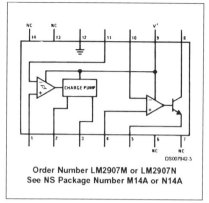

Order Number LM2907M or LM2907N
See NS Package Number M14A or N14A

LM2907 Frequency to Voltage IC
(14-pin DIL version)

Diodes

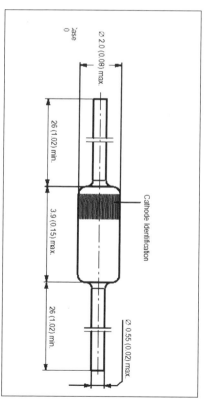

BAT-85 Schottky and most small
signal diodes.

197

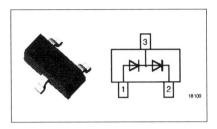

BAV-99 Dual Silicon diode

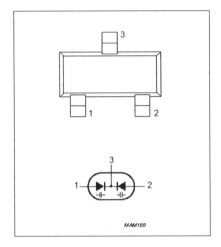

BB804 Dual Varicap diode

Index